PHYSICAL EDUCATION

(A Handbook for Teachers)

Rachna Jain

SPORTS PUBLICATION
7/26, Ground Floor, Ansari Road, Darya Ganj,
New Delhi-110 002. Ph.: (O) 55749511, 55257538
(M) 9868028838 (R) 27562163

Published by:

SPORTS PUBLICATION
H.O.: 7/26, Ground Floor, Ansari Road,
Darya Ganj, New Delhi-110 002.
B.O. C-13, Rose Apartment, Sector-14 Extn.,
Rohini, Delhi-110 085.
Ph. : (O) 55749511, 55257538 (R) 27562163, (M) 9868028838
E-mail: *ektathani@hotmail.com*
Website : www.sportspublication.trade-india.com

I.S.B.N. – 81-7879-274-5

PRINTED IN INDIA 2006

Laser Typeset by:
JAIN MEDIA GRAPHICS, Delhi-110035. Ph.: 27190244

Printed by:
CHAWLA OFFSET PRINTERS, Delhi-110052

Price: Rs. 495/-

CONTENTS

1

INTRODUCTION TO PHYSICAL EDUCATION

PHYSICAL EDUCATION IN THE BEGINNING

Physical education in the nineteenth century presents a dismal picture of drill masters, ustads and superannuated army gymnasts who knew very little of modified Swedish gymnastics and nothing more than what the army had taught them for the conditioning of uncultured adult recruits. No serious effort was made either by the Government or the educational authorities to the question of health, efficiency and harmonious development of the whole man.

ADVENT OF PHYSICAL EDUCATION ON OUR SOIL

With the dawn of the twentieth century, the first rays of light shone upon this continent to enlighten people of the importance of physical fitness and a scientific physical education. It was the YMCAs in India which played a major role in spreading the new concept.

It goes to the credit of America which produced great physical educational missionaries and the United Kingdom which sent great educationists to India. Many leaders trained at the International College of Physical Education of YMCA at Springfield (Mass) USA, have done pioneering work in the field of physical education in India and other countries in the East.

AN INSTITUTION FOR PHYSICAL EDUCATION

With the arrival in 1908 of Dr. Henry Gray as the first Physical Director of the National YMCA at Calcutta a new emphasis was given to physical education. Through lectures, demonstrations and through a programme of physical training, games and sports in the various YMCAs in India, Dr. Grey and his associated created a new interest in Physical Education of modern lines. Later, Dr. A.G. Noehren as the National Physical Director of YMCAs of India, continued the work of Dr. Gray.

A young American, H.C. Buck, then doing physical education work at Wichita, Kansas, came to India in September 1918 to take service as Physical Director at the Central YMCA, Madras. He studies the existing situation in the country, felt the great need for training leadership in the field, and established a School of Physical Education in the year 1920 at Madras, which has today blossomed into the YMCA College of Physical Education.

PHYSICAL EDUCATION FROM H.C. BUCK'S POINT OF VIEW

H.C. Buck found in physical education a field where all the races and creeds of the world can come together and meet in the worship of those qualities of love and forgiveness, beauty and splendour, truth and justice, equanimity and kindness which are essential for a good life.

In 1919, he started as a humble worker as Physical Director and co-worker with Dr. Noehren at the Central YMCA Madras, and was soon able to indicate in his statements orderliness, discipline, respect for rules and a host of other qualities essential for sportsmen and a good citizen. Buch's vision, his faith and optimism, his tenacity of purpose, his interring zeal, his geniality and inherent goodness, his limitless industry and immense capacity for leadership, were the materials which contributed to the stately steel frame of that edifice which he raised and endowed with strength and richness to the traditions it created and treasured for the betterment of the youth of India. Till about the twenties physical education was unknown to this country and its educational system. Educationists did indeed believe in the old adage "Men Sana in Corpore Sano", but all that was done in schools to put that saying into practice was to give the pupils as occasional hour of drill in the week and, where convenience permitted and facilities could be had without trouble, a team of star players in football or badminton was trained.

The instructors were ignorant and ill-paid. There was no attempt to provide for, and much less to teach games to pupils. Drill was done only outside the school hours and even that was more or less unrelated to the school curriculum. The drill master was accordingly the Cinderella of the school staff and could often be bought off or placated without difficulty by influential pupils. The drill master often used language and adopted methods which we should associate with the back streets of olden days. Even the check that drill masters wore spike of their outlook and attitude, for when they did not choose to wear their old army uniforms, they generally donned the familiar but grotesque dress peculiar to circus ringmasters of games. These drill masters knew little or nothing, nor were they interested. Further, where an attempt was made to provide facilities for play they were left to the care of someone among the teachers of the three R's and the drill masters could hardly poach upon the preserves of honorary superintendents of games. Despite the lack of any general provision for games for all pupils, headmasters and principals, book-inspired and anxious to emulate British examples, talked glibly of the many virtues of team games and the benefits accruing from pupil participation in sports.

In fact, even in this country it was a common belief that the Battle of Waterloo was won on the playfields of Eton and Harrow. No serious effort was, however, made to give thought to the questions of the health and efficiency of the school child. This cannot be considered strange in a country where not only education but even administration has tended till quite recently to function according to the convenience of the rulers, whose main aim naturally centred directly or indirectly on their own interests, rather than on the health and progress of the people.

BASIC GOALS OF PHYSICAL EDUCATION

Physical education should aim to provide skilled leadership, adequate facilities and ample time for affording full opportunity for individuals and groups to participate in situation that are physically wholesome, mentally stimulating and satisfying and socially sound. This implies a thorough understanding of the nature and needs of the participants and the implementation of a programme utilising activities and facilities catering to these interests and needs.

THE FUNDAMENTAL OBJECTIVES OF PHYSICAL EDUCATION

1. Protection and improvement of health and the development of organic fitness.
2. Increase in strength and neuro-muscular control.
3. Development of desirable social attitudes and standards or conduct.
4. Acquisition of skills, habits and attitudes in a variety of physical activities which will contribute to wholesome and enjoyable leisure pursuits.

INTERPRETATION IN PHYSICAL EDUCATION

Physical education is that part of the general education programme which is concerned with the growth, development and education of children through the medium of muscular activities. It is education of the whole child by means of physical activities. They are so selected and conducted as to influence every aspect of the child's life physically, mentally, emotionally and morally.

Some of the reasons why physical education and scientifically trained physical educators are necessary in India are the following:

1. General disinclination to exercises which develop hardihood.
2. Need of training in high ideals of sportsmanship.
3. Ignorance of sex matters.
4. Child marriage.
5. Lack of attention to sanitation.
6. Improper diet.
7. Widespread use of drugs and other forms of addiction. N.K. Mia says in his articles: "Buck and the Y.M.C.A. College of Physical Education":

But in the last analysis, if India is to be saved, she must save herself. No body cannot for ever bear all her burdens. India and Indians are best understood by her own people. This being so it seems only proper that this programme of physical regeneration should be carried on by the sons of India—Our attempt at depending upon foreign Physical Directors to do the job has been futile and the solution lies in training indigenous leadership.

We need help from developed countries like America which has the money, the manpower and the experience. All these are needed in helping India to help herself, and our prayer is that individuals in America may be made to see this opportunity to serve, each according to his talents. In spite of an abundance of acceptable interpretations and advice from authoritative writers and speakers, there is still a tendency to cling to outmoded methods and systems of physical education. Therefore, whether physical education has any place in the present social order and whether it can contribute anything of value to modern life, will depend entirely upon our intention to continue to cling tenaciously to the traditionally formalised and standardised schemes of physical education based on some artificial system of exercises.

We may assume at the outset that in any educational procedure the sensible thing to do is to be guided by the facts obtained from a study of human nature and to build up our programme in the light of the facts so discovered. It is education of the whole man, through the medium of physical activities. As such, the activities should be carefully selected and conducted.

Physical education in the past has suffered from the same defects as general education. There has been too great a tendency to follow the line of least resistance and to fit individuals and groups to preconceived schemes of work instead of fitting the programme to the interests and needs of those being educated. Such misguided procedures are not likely to bring the desired results. Both education and physical education must provide experiences that are life like and which will produce personalities capable of adjusting to the present-day social order. A study of the history of physical education reveals that much valuable time has been wasted in squabbles over the merits and demerits of various systems.

RESEARCH, EDUCATION AND PHYSICAL EDUCATION

A variety of research fronts established in the industrial sphere were the causative factor for the industrial that has taken place. In the field of humanities or the human sciences, research has contributed new frontiers of knowledge.

This is particularly true in the area of medicine, engineering, sociology and psychology. In India, physical education is a growing field and if is to be made scientific and comparable with other advanced fields such as medicine, engineering, science, agriculture, etc., it is essential that more and more research should be undertaken in this field under the available conditions.

There is no doubt that numerous research studies can be carried out on the playfield itself. Yet adequate and appropriate space is needed where sophisticated instruments can be installed and research studies conducted under controlled conditions. Education is usually regarded as acquisition of knowledge. It is defined as "the art of making available to each generation the organised knowledge of the past". It also involves "the aggregate of all the processes by means of which a person develops abilities, attitudes and other forms of positive faculties in the society in which he lives".

More than acquiring knowledge, it cultivates a cluster of attitudes and skills. The ability to think independently and clearly is of major importance. Education thus becomes a means to and end, not and end by itself. It is with a view to developing the overall personality of youth that physical education has been made a part of general education. "Education is control of the development of knowledge and formation of the whole structure of man." "Physical education is now being recognised as a part of total education, as a phase of general education and as a way of real education." Of all animals, man has been the most successful in the constant struggle against the environment. Even though he cannot run as fast as some quadrupeds, swim like dolphins, climb like apes, fly as birds do, he has been the only creature capable of defying the forces of gravity and reaching the realms of outer space.

The one factor that has enabled him to accomplish this feat is his ingenuity and intelligence in understanding the mysteries of nature. Man has consistently striven to run faster, jump higher, throw farther and have greater speed, power and strength. Physical education and sports alter the very essence of life. They shape social and human needs, bring greater goodwill and closer contact in the comity of nations. Physical education is extremely essential for helping to remove the differences between mental and physical work. The study of man and motion is a complex task. We cannot comprehend man as a whole. We know him as the macrocosm of distinct parts and the cream of creation. Today, research enjoys a prestigious place in physical education and coaching programmes.

The scholar should be fully aware of the purposes to be served by the research which he undertakes, whether it is applied or pure research. He should be able to conduct the research in an objective way. He should be able to communicate his experience, observations and findings in a cogent and clear-cut manner. Then only case the scholar justify his placement. The research worker's mission should be to conduct a research programme which will benefit the discipline of area selected by him.

The ability to analyse critically is a necessary attribute of a successful researcher.

The problems the scholars face are:

(i) Problems related to time : in the majority of cases, the completion of research takes at least four years;

(ii) Problems related to the sources of information; reference books are the only commonly available aid to research; equipment and other facilities have not been strengthened to a satisfactory extent;

(iii) The majority of scholars feel that their research has no practical application, but just serves as a stop-gap arrangement;

(iv) There is more confusion in selecting the topic than in selecting the director.

PLAY AND CHILD

In the modern world, the objective of education is the development of intellectual skills like thinking, planning and imagination, achieving social skills like competition, cooperative feeling, endurance and emotional maturity besides psychomotor skills and abilities like grip, coordination, strength, etc. In this respect, the educational objectives and processes have a great impact on physical education.

The scholarly learning which the students acquire in the classroom can have tremendous relevance and impact in the playground. The quantum and quality of learning differ from age to age. As the child grows physically and mentally, he exhibits variations of learning level. In the initial stage, educational perspective is a conglomeration of certain measures like action and rest, success and failure, nervousness and fear of facing competition.

The child may not be fully aware of the competition and may not be equipped to participate in serious competitions in all aspects. A fully grown (individual) student is mature enough to make himself ready and fit for participation in physical activities and to analyse his own performance for further rectification and improvement. A seasoned sportsman is far advanced in playing techniques, anticipating the type and nature of performance of the opponents and entering into the playfield in a well-prepared manner to face tactfully the opposing sportsman. There is every possibility for a shrewd and strategic sportsman to transform and apply the classroom knowledge and fruitful experience in the playfield and also throughout his lifetime, in whichever walk of life he may choose.

Ultimately it is quite obvious that the educational perspective of physical education programmes does help a student to lead a meaningful and disciplined life with the right convictions and attitude. It is quite clear that every child, when entering the playfield considers himself, consciously or unconsciously, as a separate and individualised entity during every moment of play. The child is demonstrating his actions with the force of his physiological and academic background. The personality traits and the knowledge learnt in the classroom are reflected in his play. Every sportsman needs a basic or minimum level of literacy and communicative skills because physical activity is controlled by written and verbal commands. Nowadays, a sportsman has to operate or use sophisticated sports equipment or gadgets for advanced training and better performance.

So, it becomes all the more important for personnel involved in games and sports, chiefly for the sportsman, to have the unique personality, basic educational status and novel scientific ideas to explore and exploit new method and openings in the vista of physical education and sports. A child is exposed to several kinds of experiences, many situations and opportunities which mould his thinking, imagination and deeds.

In the educational institutions, the educational perspective helps him to interpret and understand the experiences and outcomes of the playfields. The practical experiences from physical activities apply to a great extent in the effective performance in the classroom also. The attitude, and action of a student should be analysed in totality, taking into consideration both classroom performance and playground achievements. The psychological disorders such as dejection and frustration which affect students may be due to the direct or indirect effect of the interaction of the pleasant or unpleasant experiences that the students may have undergone. The physical educator should take the utmost care to diagnose these correctly and extend guidance and counselling. The partial and incomplete approach by the physical educator may impair the physical and psychological constitution of the child.

The crux of the problem is that the classroom teachers do not have any active hand in the practical affairs of the field and, likewise, the physical educators do not take part in the classroom teaching and other curricular programmes. So there is a yawning gap between these two. They must plan an effective solution to bridge the gap so that the students acquire harmonious, healthy and rich knowledge from the teachers of both general education and physical education. Physical education is an unparalleled domain, because it helps students to reap maximum benefits.

There have to be certain preconditions like positive biological endowment, creating positive educational goals and appropriate opportunities for the child to interact with the school in a positive manner and to be conscious of the educational outcome of such interaction. The learning of the child is dependent upon nature, environment, facilities of the educational institution, etc. There are noticeable differences between a child from a school with all the facilities and the one from a school which is not equipped with the necessary amenities and facilities. A child who emerges out of a rural school will lag behind the other children in almost every aspect. Moreover, the invaluable and formative ideas and experiences that a child learns from the inter-school and intra-school competitions also differ from situation to situation. Traits such as presence of mind, intelligence, performance in the field surely will have an impact and carry-over value and will definitely have a 'say' in their later life. The playfield can be described as a miniature classroom where many of the educational processes are going on to help them to achieve skills, performance and character traits through play interaction. Sports and games provide numerous opportunities for the players to strike up interaction between various personalities.

A player has to move with the manager, coach, referee, captains, playmates, etc. This interaction may help or hinder the purpose of physical development and educational growth. The physical educators and coaches must bear in mind factors such as individual difference and the interaction between the player and the physical activity. Then only can they render service effectively. The individual difference may be of many kinds-physiological, social, psychological, physical and educational, capacities, resources and limitations that an individual exhibits from time to time. The playfield is an open laboratory which does not have physical boundaries. Here the sky is the limit.

The playground activities inspire many young ones to fight in a healthy manner in order to achieve victory. This correlates the educational goal with that of physical education. The open-field classroom help young children to adapt themselves to failures, and frustration, victory and defeat, individual honour and group triumph and emotional ups and downs. The playfield can reject players, push them to its boundaries and make them wish to lose. It also, at times depresses, exhilarates and stimulates. It sorts out the individual players according to their capacity, performance and status. The educational aim of play at a given moment may be to teach the rules of the games, to teach the physical activities, etc. The educative atmosphere in the institutions may create a spirit of competition and cooperation, domination, democracy, stimulation and depression.

The participants may not have the same mental calibre or interest in physical events. The intensity of seriousness, and the degree of genuine interest on the part of the participant sportsman may vary according to the personality and ature of the sportsman. It is high time that we plan meticulously the various ways to learn the physical activities in a scientific manner, like our predecessors, so that we can hand over a standardised knowledge to our younger generation.

Hence, physical activities become sufficiently educational, if they develop this capacity to inherit from our predecessors and extend to our progeny. The continuous emphasis of the moral approach and attempt of the physical education policy will bring about solid progress. Physical education helps to provide this continuity in action and thought. The learning that is taking place inside the classroom should be continued and carried on outside also. No doubt, the playground is the agency and medium that offers continuity to education.

There are other agencies such as the family, neighbourhood, professional playgroups, government, mass media, to give continuity and perpetuate the career of people by inducting them into the educational sphere. The physical educator and coach should select appropriate physical activities, and ancillary equipment that will improve the spirit of commitment of the professional. The general pattern of sports and games and all the inherent programmes have been structured from the sphere of general education. The policies, and programmes of physical education should always be in accordance with general education policies. The school and the playground play a predominant role in the formation of a strong personality in children as they spend the major part of the day time in schools.

GENERAL POINT OF VIEW

In ancient times, physical activity was part and parcel of man behaviour in his every endeavour. The modern man, even after realising and relishing the higher values and fruits of physical education, unfortunately neglects physical activity. Trained leaders of physical education have failed in advocating or defining the concept of physical education. They have defined it in terms of sports and games.

Thus, the tremendous effects and sacred values of physical education have been reduced to the very minimum. In the recent times, the concept of physical education has been accorded due importance, attention and recognition.

Experts from various quarters have started patronising the one-time neglected field on realising its merits. The old-timers are of the opinion that physical education was meant for those who were gifted with physical strength and prowess. Such misconceptions are no more valid. Now the trend is that physical education is a must for every human being at all age levels for a complete life. It has wonderful potentialities and tremendous a virtues to give to every man under the sun.

As time passes, there occurred very constructive literary works on themes like specialised and specific games, its history and contribution to health and recreation, growth and development of physical education and allied fields. But, to our surprise, it has still not been considered as an academic subject in the true sense and remains simply either an extracurricular or extra-educational activity despite the considerable amount of literature on the subject. It is a healthy indication if a discipline grows in its structure, dimension and application.

The expansion of physical education is quite possible if it draws concepts and laws from other allied branches of knowledge. Physical education has enriched its content and scope by deriving sports from medicine and yoga, from philosophy. A part from such induction of allied knowledge, there have been developments of the principal concepts, improvements of the pattern of games, in the design of equipments, playing conditions, techniques of coaching methods, methodical organisation and administration, the use of tests and measurements in physical education, etc.

This remarkable improvement has helped those who are directly or indirectly involved in the field of physical education. Researches in physical education conducted all over the world in the past years, have provided highly beneficial ideas and novel advantages. In the hoary past, all over the world exercises were mostly associated with the rigorous training of the military services. Man and his actions should be in accordance with mother nature for a healthy and happy existence. Physical education is largely advocated in western countries to promote the well-being of the population at large, right from the young stage for effective functioning of the human internal systems as well as effective functioning of the body and for efficient performance on the sports arena.

The basic principles of natural movement are consistent with that of general education and were formulated as a direct response to the recognition that out older practices and ideas in physical education were consistent with the modern philosophy of education. Philosophy and physical education are as interrelated and inseparable as two sides of the same coin and they play a dynamic role in shaping the life of an individual or an individual of in a group. The spectacular professional career of a physical educator enlivens and enlightens the mentality and mode of action of the young students in the high school and colleges, particularly in the matters relating to sports career.

The impact of concrete and compact concepts of physical education eventually makes a break through in their outlook and day to day life.

As the first phase, the physical educators are expected to develop mental attitudes and skills and undergo hardship, stress and strain besides sacrifices. The physical educators should take the initiative to render the service of uplifting the profession and the young student community at large, bearing in mind the following key points; code of behaviour, professional attitude, philosophy of the profession, professional commitment and job satisfaction which are to be given due stress in the course of his accomplishments.

The physical educator has to march a long way for transforming his personal and technical personality for the cause of the cherished field of physical education, as well as the positive transformation of the domain of physical education. The physical educator has been entrusted with a great mission of teaching for the betterment of his students and his profession. However, he has not been provided with the ideal type of professional training. He does not enjoy the privilege of having well-defined clients to render service to. His clients are in a way vague, willy nilly and general in nature. The clients do not come forward with specific and clearcut defects, deficiencies and problems. In spite of these drawbacks most of the physical educators do spot out the innate and latent talents of the students and inspire and encourage them to specialise in specific areas. They enrich the trainees or students by feeding appropriate theoretical knowledge as well.

EDUCATIONAL POINT OF VIEW

Educational principles are patterned in such a way that the students in schools and colleges are moulded into complete personalities by means of guided participation. The child has to be looked after and nourished systematically and scientifically by the teachers at various levels. The medium for this sacred task is the well-designed and balanced physical education programmes.

According to scientific educational techniques, the teachers should pick out the positive as well as negative aspects of the students under them, and do their best to analyse and synthesise the psychological and emotional demands of the students. Guidance and counselling can be rendered to the students for their betterment by the physical education teachers. The students should be trained to transfer the skills or talents acquired to the other domains in which they may involve themselves in later phases of life. It is quite appropriate to have strict and stipulated norms of physical efficiency for admitting the students into educational institutions, though it may sound rigid, unconventional and impractical in day-to-day life.

This pattern of admission will hold good in due course and help to realise the true aims and objectives of physical education and make use reap the real fruits there of. We can then produce totally developed personalities more easily. Educational commentators, academic experts and other critics question the contributory role of physical education and its related subjects in vogue in producing a substantial positive effect in the mind and behaviour of the people. If it does not prove to be good, competitive sports and games can be brought to a halt, which are just a national waste.

It is more purposeful if we plan meticulously for mass participation, group involvement, and mass level fitness and health programmes along with great emphasis on recreational activities which are highly conductive in making a strong, solid, cultured and healthy society. Education has been defined as a change, modification of an adjustment on the part of the student as a result of fruitful experiments and experiences.

Physical education is called an integral part of the total educational process which combines the physical, social and psychological aspects of man's life, through well-directed physical activities. There are other sciences like physics and medicine which have enriched the core and content of physical education.

The educational principles chiefly aim at producing well bread and well-balanced children who will adjust with and adapt to the real problems in their future lifestyle. The planned programme should be congenial to the philosophy and goal of the individuals, groups or communities for whom it is designed. Meaningless theory and unsuitable activities should be eliminated because they fail to satisfy and fulfil the requirement of the pupils for personality growth.

The original thrust of the educational policy is aimed at the improvement of academic standards thereby enriching the intellectual spheres of the students. This concept, when put into practice in the past, did not come up to expectations for reasons like imbalanced character development and other serious handicaps which could have been avoided, to a great extent, if combined efforts had been undertaken to influence the young children as well as college-going students in the right academic perspectives. The total development of the individual is of prime importance.

The experts in the field of education must find out ideal means, methods and agencies through which the total development can be achieved in practical life. The various physical activities are the media, which are considered as educational objectives and means to achieve the total objective of integrated development. The physical education policies and programmes, along with education-oriented approaches, will successfully create the required personality traits among the students.

It is high time that we totally discard the traditional concepts of physical education which develop mutual indifference, confrontation and isolation between education and physical education. Education with its dynamic nature and thrust towards improvement should concentrate on imparting valuable knowledge in health education, movement education, recreation, physical education, vocational education, fine arts, etc., to the children at early period of their lives.

If we look back to the concepts of education of the ancient Spartan government, we come to know that the aim of education was to produce men of action and individual physical excellence so that the individual could be put to the service of the country especially in times of emergency and war. In those days, human power was chiefly utilised for military purposes as countries were waging wars for survival constantly, and to establish their supremacy over the others. Apparently the idea was to keep the citizens physically sound so as to live life to the flues and they sought wholesome activities that aimed at harmonious development of the body. In short, the whole educational pattern was to channelise the youth towards military objectives.

However, the aim today is to develop the total personality of man for a better life. These above said educational objectives can be achieved provided the programmes of physical education fit into the educational perspective of the total system. The dynamic operations of the educational system should be well understood by men who are entrusted with the work of gearing up the administrative machinery of physical education. The physical educators should take utmost care that they must not over emphasize the importance of the physical aspects of the game situation and the educational values should be developed among the students for fuller growth. Students may become completely balanced and grown up in every aspect only if both the values are developed hand in hand.

As a matter of fact, physical education has not been given educational orientation because the recreational aspects enjoy more importance than the educational aspects. The formulation of the various physical activities must be done taking the educational principles into account. The general education pattern must yield to certain positive changes and transformation in its structure and policy for this purpose. The key points such as the developmental characteristics of students, the principle of correlation between academic subjects and physical activities, the principle of student-teacher ratio, etc., should be give due place in the physical education curriculum. The sole purpose of physical activities should be the fulfilment of the higher values of general education.

PHYSICAL EDUCATION

Physical movements are a biological necessity. Physical education has devised organised games and sports in a systematic way within the educational institutions. A student learns a lot when he takes part in any event. He gradually learns to perform in a perfect manner, after repetition. He understands the nature and inherent techniques of a phenomenon by the trial and error methods, thereby mastering the do's and don'ts of a particular area. Thus, an individual is facilitated in having a wide scope of learning by himself through the medium of physical activities in an educational atmosphere. This may be called the self-analysis function of scientific physical activity.

The educational values of physical education can be acquired in the open classroom, i.e., the playground where the instructor conducts various types of activities which provide ample opportunities for character development, play-interaction, shouldering responsibility and practising the art acquired before. The participation in the field activities direct and educates the students. The classroom and the playground are the twin places where the students can experiment with their innate talents in order to evaluate themselves and put into practice their worth.

There is the possibility also to compensate by performing well in the field in case anybody is weak in classroom achievements, or a student may even retain the same high position in both the places. Physical education is a superb field wherein ample opportunities are created for the development of complete personality through coordinated physical activities.

The unique feature of physical education programmes is that participants willingly engage themselves without any kind of hesitation, inhibitions and reservation. No doubt, other academic and social media of the school like the curriculum, classroom, administrative machinery and examination system also play a significant role in the formation of wholesome personality, but physical education contributes a vital part of the total general education pattern. Physical Education had to pass through a number of ordeals, and tribulations to its achieve present prestigious status.

Physical education programmes were considered to be the extracurricular and evening-hour recreational activities in those days, whereas it enjoys an enviable position now because researches and innovations were made in curricula and in implementation of the designed activities.

Moreover, it has been proved that there is a direct relationship between scholastic standing and the physical performance in the field. So, also, the physical educators in schools and colleges now enjoy honour and professional status and they are on the faculty councils and university committees.

This clearly indicates that physical education has been recognised and universally accepted as being on part with other departments of knowledge. Physical education has many wings such as athletics associations, amateur associations, professional units, coaching centres, etc., in which specialised personnel are working hard for the improvement of the specific purposes.

It is a healthy sign if there is meaningful and coordinated integration for the overall prosperity of the entire field. The question arises: Is there integration and coordination between general education and physical education? Undoubtedly, a congenial atmosphere has been established between physical education and general education.

Moreover, the wide gap has been almost bridged. In schools and colleges, physical education programmes have been made compulsory for all the students and thus a mutual interdependence between them has been well established. It is not wrong to say that physical education and general education are inspirable. The physical educators of today have been entrusted with greater responsibilities in keeping with the changed curriculum. In the past, physical education was thought of as improving the physique, strength and motor skills, whereas it now aims at improving the overall personality of a man. It is a healthy sign that physical education has been accorded the right place which has enlarged its aims and objective. It is the moral duty of the whole physical education machinery to tone itself so as to make a breakthrough in this field.

The main and very important aim of physical education is to create ideal opportunities for young students at various levels to acquire the true and all-round perfection and development in every aspect. The main objectives of the multifarious programmes of physical education is to produce responsible and rational citizen who act wisely throughout their lives. We have not yet succeeded in this particular aspect and angle. There is no shadow of doubt that we have to go a long way in order to realise the goals of physical education.

GENERAL EDUCATION AND PHYSICAL EDUCATION

The progress of life and physical education are inseparable. Physical education is an integral part of general education as well as that of our life. In view of the vital role that it plays in our very life, we should have recognised it and adopted it effectively in general education. It is high time that we give it the right status. There cannot be good results in the limited time allotted to the physical education classes. The time must be sufficiently increased for the efficient and effective learning of the higher values of physical education.

It should get the academic status of a full-fledged branch of knowledge which will pave the way for a renaissance in all spheres of general education. The leaders of physical education blesses with foresight are striving hard to achieve this ideal. The ideal changes and reformative amendments in the principles of physical education should be carried out after deep thought and analytical scrutiny, taking into consideration three vital aspects, namely, the scope of physical education as a full-fledged academic discipline, professional ethics and the relationship with other domains.

Physical education has a relationship and correlation with different academic fields. It has to draw various physical, biochemical and mechanical laws from other disciplines for its enrichment. Thus the content of this field is abundantly rich. Professional ethic should take a new dimensional approach and physical education can no more be an island away from the mainstream of education. The chief aim is the all round development and fuller growth of children.

Physical education cannot survive unless it receives unstinted co-operation and generous help from other disciplines. The affinity and relationship between general education and physical education have fallen into oblivion in the practical sense. Thus both exist physically together but are functionally apart. Both must go hand in hand in order to produce the desired result in the personality development of children at all levels. The physical educators should be conscious of the importance to be given to the educational perspective in physical activity. Opportunities should be open to all the pupils in educational institutions for fuller growth and prosperity.

It is important that carefully chosen and meticulously planned physical activities should be included in the curriculum to enhance the active participation of the children for this development of their personality traits. It is important to evaluate the contribution of general education to the development of the culture, attitude and behaviour of the people of this country. Have we succeeded in this great task? We have made considerable improvement in the physical education programmes which have really played an important role in discriminating knowledge, liberating the mind and improving skills, promoting free thinking and encouraging creative talents and developing positive attitudes towards change and order. Society is expecting a long from general education. A player should be analysed and judged from several angles. The physical educator should scout the all round performance of a player not only in the sportsfield but also in the classroom and elsewhere. The player's behaviour patterns must be scrutinised for further psychological stabilisation.

There should be an ideal relationship between the classroom teachers and physical educators so that both can arrive at an analytical conclusion about the abilities, interest, limitations and scope of each individual student and his participation in the school activities. This system of studying the students helps the physical educator to assess the motor skills of the individual before the individual is permitted to practise in the specialised area. The physical educator establishes a close relationship with the teachers of other disciplines regarding nutrition, health, diseases, safety measures, first aid, etc.

The physical educator has to cover the topics like physiology, physics, sports, medicine, first aid and he is also involved in mathematical concepts like duration of time, counting measurements, sequences, evaluation, etc. Further, he has to evolve social concepts that may be developed during healthy athletic competitions and games. He should ask the students to give their views and comments after the game is over.

In this way, physical education is a part of general education. Physical education is passing through a difficult period because the State and policy makers do not come forward enthusiastically to make it an essential part of general education. The time allotted for students at lower levels as well as higher levels is not sufficient at all. Naturally, the students cannot benefit much from physical education in most schools and colleges. If at all students spend their evenings on the games field, it may be the "chosen group" participating in the school games, inter-class matches and inter-school tournaments which are purely carried on a voluntary basis.

The pity is that the fruits of physical education do not reach all the students. Moreover, there is no uniform pattern in the schools regarding the effective thrust on physical education with the result that it is not given the due place and importance and has thus become and matter of convenience.

Generally, the teachers of general education as well as of physical education feel that general education and physical education are distinct and separate entities and do not have common educational elements. This is the cause for several serious misconceptions among the educated masses as well as the public. They fail to recognise the interrelationship and interdependence without which the very purpose of general education is defeated. It is very interesting to note that both the subject teacher and the physical educator deal with the same material, namely the student. The unity of organism, and the interaction between the parts are confirmed in research findings.

The integration of youth personalities in educational institutions is safeguarded and promoted to the optimum level only if the forces, of these twin, related fields act on the student community. It is a fact that the examination system and the present pattern of education contribute in making the student panic-stricken, perturbed and crippled as regards the spontaneous development of personality traits.

General education cannot afford to forego the unique services of the physical educator. He is an asset not only to the educational institutions but also to the students because his chief work is to promote their physical health as well as their intellects, emotions, sociable character, cognitive and recreational abilities.

The days are not far off when physical education will identify itself with general education. At present, this ideal identification is mostly at a verbal level. Though it is popularly said that physical education is an integral part of general education, yet it is so only theoretically. It is however very gratifying to know that a favourable climate is now gradually being created to establish a close rapport. It is necessary that physical education should have devised a clear-cut basic concept which is conductive for such renovative outcome and mutual enrichment. This healthy relationship between general subjects and physical education should blossom in the day-to-day routine of schools and colleges which will contribute to the balanced growth, psychological stability and positive outlook of the young students.

The terms "physical education" make us understand the educational perspective as well as physical values. But in practice, unfortunately, we are prone to missing the educational value that are derived from physical education. In this way we miss the right perspective. The foundations of physical education and the preconditions of a proper educational perspective have not been efficiently planned and effectively executed.

This deficient condition has led to academic chaos and confusion in its implementation, as result of which a corrective formula is to be sought to put physical education on the right track. It is obvious that physical education has a great role to play in order to achieve the goals of education. But the physical educators are not aware of the potentialities it possesses.

The correct approach, practical manipulations and organisational devices are not to be carried out in every educational institution by the individual physical educator alone. Both physical education and general education are inseparable and the existence and execution of one is not only unhealthy but also creates undesirable tendencies among the children.

Physical education should always produce an educational value which is superb and ideal in every respect. The necessary prerequisites should made available for the successful implementation of physical education. Here educational perspective is a precondition. There is no guarantee that we may succeed to a great extent just because of the existence of the educational perspective. Moreover, there are other factor which determine the possibility of the correct educational perspective.

They are:-

(i) certain physiological and biological endowments,

(ii) The educational institution and its multifarious on-going activities,

(iii) The ample scope for interaction between groups and individuals.

These three factors can make a correlation between physical education and education for the purpose of transfer of learning from one to another which may not always be simple in practical situations. The educational values that the children learn from physical activities are different depending upon the teachers coaches, facilities, playmates and available equipments.

The type of educational experience acquired differs from one game to the other according to the nature, movement pattern, equipment and ground as different technical and biomechanical principle are involved in them. The scoring procedures, strategy and technical personnel vary according to the game.

Thus the students engaged in different physical activities receive several kinds of educational values. A gifted and brilliant student may excel both in academic performance as well as in the spheres of games and sports. It is a golden opportunity for the students to have the playing field as the educating unit where they are exposed to educative phenomena such as trial and error learning, goals and achievements levels, appreciation and punishment, psychological stability and sportsmanship qualities. If physical activities are efficiently organised, they may positively improve the physical standards of students. Physical education program, like competitions between the various groups in and out of the educational institutions really help to enrich their psychological aspects.

In schools and colleges, a meritorious sports performance is given due importance in matters of admission and promotions. Physical education promotes educational perspectives as it produces direct impact on the teaching learning process, organisational and administrative aspects. This inductive function of physical education is possible only if the activities are properly planned and strictly implemented. It is not possible to give a clear-cut definition of the term "education". It may mean more than an ocean.

It is incorrect to say that education takes place inside physical buildings or only in a limited area. It may occur in any place. The educational institutions provide opportunities for the students to spend a major portion of their time and learn the programmed and framed knowledge. In everybody's case, the institutionalised education has great impact on the formation of personality. The motto, systems and customs followed in a particular institution are reflected in the attitude and behaviour of a student' life. Though physical education is an integral part of general education, it also, to a great extents supports and supplements the aims and objectives of general education.

It is a heavenly blessing that the coordinated work of general education and physical education do not contradict each other at any juncture; thus there is a greater possibility of realising the aims of education is general through the various designed programmes of physical education.

Thus, it goes without saying that every physical educator should be well-versed with the precepts of general education. Physical education should not be restricted to training in sports and games. It should play a wider role in overall education of society. It is high time that the essential values and idealistic principles of various domains of learning should be brought into the mainstream of physical education to frame an integrated programme of schooling to achieve complete and comprehensive values in the educational set-up. Both general education and physical education have a common task, i.e., to promote the all-round development of the child, in their respective ways. The product to be shaped and moulded is the child.

The physical educator should possess necessary prerequisites for interpreting the psychological, social and physical aspects of the total structure of schooling so that physical activities can be selected on the basis of the need, interest and abilities of the individual students and the educational objectives of the school.

The educational basis of physical education should define the scope of physical education as well as form the proper guidelines to match the student with the activities relevant to schooling. Physical education, which is indeed a dynamic field, cannot afford to function in isolation in schools and colleges without associating itself with other connected disciplines. The field of physical education involves not only students at various levels but also several personnel like the participants, parent, audience, administrators, and physical educators. So physical education is unique in this aspect because it establishes the interaction and also the interpersonal relationship between many personalities through physical activities, thus playing a predominant role in the total educational process. The physical educator must possess positive insight into his profession and have thorough knowledge about physical education as an educational process. It makes him view the player from an educational point of view.

The player who faces victory or defeat well, who walks out of the field in protest, the physically disadvantaged, the student who withdraws from the field, the school champion, his playmates and his opponents, his captain, his coach, his officials and audience are all part of the play. So it is better that the physical educator masters the educational forces and the influences of the educational atmosphere on the player's performance and on his own coaching or training.

The competitions conducted on the field should inculcate the spirit of sportsmanship and healthy competition. The constructive competitions are designed to produce among the players educative values. The higher values emerge through the interaction of individual participants in the sports and games.

Thus, strong character is and exemplary personalities are evolved on the playfield. The behavioural methods and social science have long been of importance and interest to those concerned with sports and physical education. Great emphasis has been laid on the intensification of academic study in physical education with respect to educational objectives and their interpretation which has resulted exciting experience novel ideas, meaning, concepts and workable suggestions are evolved for physical educator in the classroom and the coach in the playground.

The physical educator should be prepared to accept and adapt to these innovative ideas. The playfield is an open-air classroom where the children go with their unique ways of life, abilities and limitation and acquire emotional stability, trial and error learning and character formation. The physical educator creates through various physical activities, an educative climate from which the children learn a lot for life along, with health habits and recreative values. A physical educator should therefore have knowledge of both physical and general education.

INTERDISCIPLINE RELATIONSHIP

No nascent discipline is rich in its structure and content. It has to grow with time. The experiments and research conducted explore the possibilities for further growth and enrichment. In this process, it has to make collaborative work with other disciplines from which concepts and professional formulae can be borrowed for its enlargement and application. The interdisciplinary sharing of ideas and joint efforts are applicable to any profession.

Physical education is not an exception because if it acts in isolation its scope and growth are adversely affected. Some sort of mutual analysis and collaborative research work will therefore help to enrich the profession substantially. The field of physical education is ever, growing in all aspects. It is in the process of enriching its major principles and premises deriving the related concepts and laws from other domains so that it can become an independent academic discipline.

The physical education teacher must be quite conversant with the new scientific formulae that are adopted from time to time to impart up-to-date qualitative education. Valuable information in the form of various physical and scientific laws becomes a part and parcel of physical education. The physical educator should earnestly strive to learn the fresh knowledge and techniques so that he can teach the students and can himself be recognised as an asset of the institution, not only by the student community but also by the staff who belong to other departments and by the community at large. He should not be content with the knowledge that he has acquired from the professional institutions as well as from books and training courses. The physical educator should also strive hard to evolve his own methods to realise the aims and objectives of our field.

In reality society expects more from the physical educators than what is being rendered by them. This calls for greater interest, dedicated service and genuine commitments on the part on the physical educators. The educational set up in the schools and colleges will yield the desired result only if general education and physical education make a wholehearted coordinated effort in implementing the programmes successfully.

General education cannot alone accomplish the onerous task of effectively educating the younger ones. There is no doubt that physical education is part and parcel of the mainstream of general education. Physical educators stress more on active participation and not on winning or losing. The matter in which the participants take part in competitions is more commended and appreciated. This applied to any profession. But qualitative work is admired and recognized in any walk of life rather than more quantity and volume of work personal gain is not the criterion but service to the common man and profession is all the more important. Idealistic principles will make the physical educators more dedicated towards developing the character of student.

The pleasure and satisfaction that we derive from hard work, dedicated service and professional commitments are definitely unique and unparalleled. A committed individual considers his profession a field where he has to put in wholehearted effort and genuinely attempt to explore new avenues of advancement. It is a thrilling experience for a dedicated physical educator to engage himself in the development of the profession. No doubt, the job satisfaction is personal and subjective. The professional curriculum must be planned in such a way that the trainees are given ample opportunities to educate themselves.

PROFESSIONALISM AND PROFESSIONAL ETHICS

Physical education aims at the all-round development of human being, i.e., young children and adults. In the field of physical education higher virtues and sacred and sublime qualities are instilled in the minds of the students. Physical educators play a predominant role in this aspect. They rank next to the parents in imparting decency and decorum to young ones. So, the physical educator should understand that his profession needs a specific type of professional behaviour. An individual can afford to lose both wealth and health, but certainly not his character. So also an individual profession cannot afford to lose its character, namely "professional image" which emerges from the plans and behaviour of the profession as well as the professional.

The community at large must certify the worth and condition of any profession and not the personnel within the profession itself. The combined and coordinated efforts of all the persons at all levels can build up a positive professional image. A single man, can by no means, succeed in this great task. Honesty and integrity of the physical educators will do a lot in this regard. The professional image is nothing but the general view that people have about a profession. Inherently, it is a psychological impression after constant and careful scrutiny of the profession. If a particular individual does not observe the code of professional ethics faithfully, he not only harms his own personal image but also ruins the already established image of the profession. Professionalisation opens up a good number of opportunities and advantageous vistas for the physical education teacher to recognise and face new problems connected with his subject in an appropriate manner.

The physical educators are trained in such a way that they are well equipped professionally to adjust and adapt to the new changes and professional regulations that are introduced from time to time. It is evident that the regulations can participate in a healthy manner in the interdisciplinary approaches and intellectual discussions with the teachers of other academic disciplines.

At present, this intellectual interaction is not very much in practice, because of the language problem or the limited acquaintance with other disciplines. Hence to further our own interest of getting accepted by other professionals from other disciplines, we should be professionalised in our discipline and be recognised with due honour as fellow teachers in the totality of the entire educational system.

It is clearly understood now that professional ethics include

(i) a code of conduct,

(ii) the philosophy of the profession,

(iii) a dignity of work,

(iv) a professional attitude,

(v) a commitment and

(vi) job satisfaction

Professional ethics can be called a psychological state of mind derived out of a voluntary exposure to a profession. Hasty action, likes and dislikes, personal attachments, sentimental influences and biased opinions have no place in a profession and an individual must take up his profession as a noble one and give it his due regard and respect.

A true and ideal professional always seeks to do something in his cherished field as his contribution and this professional thirst does not end till he creates a suitable environment for the betterment of the existing conditions of the profession. A committed physical educator is an asset to his discipline and he can be entrusted with confidential responsibilities and professional commitments because he will be prepared to make all-out attempts for utilising his potentialities and talents for the betterment of his profession.

The achievement in any academic discipline is due to such committed individuals. It is quite obvious that a trained professional in any branch of knowledge, especially in physical education, is bound to develop and possess his or her own attitude about the profession he has embraced for either livelihood or service. The physical educator should avoid forming subjective attitudes. The individual must analyse the overall situation and the impact of it before forming final attitudes, judgement and decisions.

This can be achieved only when an individual is able to estimate the real situations, and infer or interpret them with an open mind and welcome these situations irrespective of his personal likes and dislikes. Professional ethic includes the practical attitudes of the person towards his profession and the estimation and value that he attaches to it. The healthy attitudes about the profession to which an individual is wedded must duly generate the right type of spirit, drive which ultimately leads to the desired target.

Physical education involves group competition, the social gathering and togetherness of a host of individuals who try hard for individual as well as common goals wherein we find mixed causes and effects such as competition and cooperation, winning and losing, risk and safety. The element of risk involved in the field of physical education right from the training phase till the actual competition is to be borne in mind by the different personnel involved in physical education and sports namely of coaches, managers and sportsmen.

The ethical aspects of a profession should be flexible, functional and operational so as to be conductive to attaining higher and holistic virtues and values. A rigid set of professional ethics may not produce the desired result. Moreover the tremendous toil and dedicated service rendered by many become futile and fruitless. The physical educators must, as far as possible, try to follow these ethics. It is necessary to provide better working conditions and privileges to the physical educators so as to motivate them. The distribution of duties and responsibilities amongst various segments of the community makes the administrative machinery strong and smooth. The real strength of any profession lies not only in its productivity but perhaps, more so, in its ethical behaviour. Productivity is discernible whereas the effect of ethical behaviour assumes long-term significance.

Physical education can in no way boast of having the professional ethics that every other profession has been fortunate enough to possess. To cite an example, professions like medicine and law have well laid out codes of professional ethic which enhance their morale and promote their image.

As these two professions have unique roles to play in the modern world, numerous other professions too have got a predominant part to play. Physical education ethics do inspire the physical educators to participate in the professional programmes and variety of commitments in wholesome ways in order to achieve the aims and objectives of physical education.

When the physical educators fail to follow the professional ethics, they are bound to create problems of great magnitude. They may not understand the disadvantage and serious ill-effects that arise on account of the breach of the professional ethics in the beginning but in the long run it leads to the disorganisation of their own personality because of the continuous development of themselves complex and finally their behaviour cannot be justified either by themselves or by observes. It is no exaggeration to say that the absence of professional ethics causes inconsistent attitude and behaviour patterns among the physical educators. This sorry state of affairs in the field of physical education breeds conflicts, chaos, unwanted comments from others and an unpleasant atmosphere at the end.

It is crystal clear that physical educators should strictly follow the ethical values and virtues. Professional ethics denotes professional standards and norms of conduct for people who have dedicated themselves to serve the community at large through these coordinated programmes. The rules and regulations that are farmed in any profession serve like a guiding star to the people who are directly or indirectly involved.

The ethical formulate maintain the moral standard of the general social attitude and way of life. The professionals have personal ambition to achieve. In this process of dedicated service, the physical educators have to sacrifice their personal benefits. Such sacrifices and dedicated involvement by the physical educators contribute a lot to the growth of the profession.

The individual should be prepared to accept the great task for the sake of bringing honour and glory to the profession. The codes of a field are a strong base on which the future of the profession, as well as of the personnel, involved is dependent to a great extent. Professional ethics should be given top priority especially in the organisation and administration of professional concepts in an educational institution.

It vividly points out the do's and don'ts thereby helping the physical educators to get rid of the areas of conflicts and controversy. The physical educators are quite aware of, and conversant with the ideal ways and means of putting into practice the systematic approaches and ideal method of the profession. The guiding principles of professional ethics are a "must" for specific action and accomplishment in the everchanging routine and roles of physical educators. The physical educators should welcome and appreciate the professional codes for the betterment of their profession. It is important to note that rules and concepts are for the profession.

The professional ethics emerge within the framework of the profession itself which may be the result of the experiences acquired and the amalgamated opinions and constructive views of the co-physical educators of various correlated backgrounds. The physical educators are morally bound to observe professional ethics as there are no hard and fast rules to punish the defaulters in case they fail to follow. But the social pressures from the professional associations, etc., are the usual social penalties for violating professional ethics. Every physical educator is expected to be more responsible to adhere to the ethics framed. Though the code of professional ethics is applicable to teachers in general, the physical educators are particularly expected to practice it sincerely so as to set a good example for others.

There are lot of opportunities in physical education programmes such as fair play, good sportsmanship, cooperation, unselfishness, regard for rules of games and fellowship, etc. The physical educators should lead a clean academic as well as social life, failing which they earn a bad name for the physical education community and the profession too.

PHILOSOPHY

The most important professional hurdle that we find in the world of today is that interested and dedicated individuals do not join the field of physical education. The physical educators are therefore largely misfits who may not be competent enough to deliver the goods.

Physical education is the last resort for incompetent individuals who have no aptitude for the profession. Some individuals knowingly take temporary shelter under its fold. This sorry state of affairs generates wavering minds and indifference on the part of these. These professionals can always contribute something positively to the profession and not the wayward individuals. This type of superficial expansion is temporary and detrimental to the health and improvement of the profession.

The precondition for any professional growth is thus the number of committed professionals who can discharge their professional responsibilities diligently and willingly. An individual can switch over to another profession but an intentional stay in a profession as a "pastime" may considerably ruin the growth of the profession and its very existence. In these days, physical educators work mainly for monetary benefits. If not all, most of them do not have or develop the requisite enthusiasm, sincerity and dedication. If we trace the development of any profession, we find that it is because many dedicated souls have worked relentlessly.

It is, no doubt, a challenging and tough task for those who wish to make physical education an independent academic discipline in this vast nation. Such sagacious leaders may have to face troubles and initial impediments, but they can gradually achieve their goal provided they have strong will to face the hurdles in their path.

PHILOSOPHY AND PHYSICAL EDUCATION

Invariably all the branches of knowledge emerge from philosophy which vividly indicates the vital role that philosophy plays at every phase in all walks of life. We cannot separate or segregate philosophy from any discipline.

Physical education has or has to have the essential elements and tenets of philosophy, as it has a predominant part in the development of the total personality of a child. General education does have the relevant maximum relationship with philosophy. Philosophical analysis and values have contributed considerably to the formation of educational practice.

Motivation plays a vital part in encouraging the students, trainees and the physical educators themselves to gain inspiration and intellectual information and must work towards providing an independent status to the subject but not at the cost of discarding the role of philosophy in physical education.

In today's changing society, there must be a sound philosophy of physical education for the profession to survive and flourish. Philosophy is a process through which physical educators search for truths, reality and values. It is only through philosophy that physical educators are able to stuck the meaning, nature, importance and source of values in physical education. Philosophy guides the physical educator in determining the aims, objectives, principles and content of physical education and provides a logical means of determining whether or not it is providing worth while services in the education of human beings. A professional philosophy has the superb inherent ability to inspire the professional to act with vigour and vitality, conviction and contemplation to the fullest possible extent.

The essential elements of philosophy are eventually reflected in his mind, words and deed. The mind, local system and psychomotor system generate positive thinking, positive speaking and positive doing. The congenial blend of these three vital aspects, goes astray if the individual does not strictly follow the professional ethics and philosophical values in actual practice. It is of the utmost importance that the training systems include both the professional ethics as well as the philosophy along with other departments of knowledge in the professional institutions. Otherwise, the training is an incomplete one which produces imbalances and inconsistencies among the physical educators.

Ever since the recorded history, philosophy has solid and strong foundation for almost all domains of knowledge. Physical education is no exception. Educational thought is influenced by the five major philosophies, viz., idealism, realism, pragmatism, naturalism and existentialism. A physical educator must have the basic knowledge of the concept of philosophy that can be practised in everyday life.

Any physical educator who has mastered or has been blessed inherently with this gift can successfully do a better job in the institutions and can better match the students and sports appropriately, instead of falling into the trap of mechanical and routine working. The physical educator should strive to inculcate in the young minds of the students a well-balanced philosophical outlook vis-a-vis the overall sports programmes. The field and concept of physical education do not enjoy any remarkable reputation and important status as most people are not convinced of the importance of physical education in day-to-day life.

There have been many great men in every field who were not physically strong. So, there is a school of thought that the physical weakness may not be a hindrance or hurdle to achieving greatness or name. It is not correct to say that physically weak people develop other compensatory capacities either to be on par with the normal ones or to excel them in every aspect. Most people are not conscious of the necessity of living a wholesome and healthy life. In ordinary life, men like to reach the pinnacle of greatness by hook or by crook.

The vital point of healthy living is ignored or totally discarded. But the very same people whole heartedly practise the physical fitness assignments. It is of interest to trace the historical development of physical education. Many scientists, philosophers and psychologists have propounded theories of physical education in depth and breadth in the light of scientific principles. Aristotle made an extensive study of the systems of the human body and its practical functions in relation to physical activities.

Physical education vividly depicts the ever-growing social changes and the changes caused in the structure and implementation of objectives of education. Its nature and content open new avenues for experimentation and exploration in the field which will pave the way for its total development. It cannot be accorded the status of an academic discipline as it does not satisfy the prerequisites at present.

But physical educators are striving ceaselessly to establish its worth. Though we may succeed in making physical education a full-fledged academic discipline, it will not function as an independent discipline unless there is a drastic move on the part of the government to promote it. Physical educators have arrived at the conclusion, after serious discussions and analysis, that physical activities have definite correlation and interrelationship with other branches of knowledge.

This had led to the promotion of the nature, purpose status and scope of physical education. The leaders of physical education have done their best to explore the influences of various social, physical, cultural and psychological phenomena upon physical activities. This is not sufficient. A strong nation wide educational policy is required to amalgamate the various factors to bring about sequential coherence among the various faculties which can stir up human activity and the acquisition of skills.

We cannot but admit the fact that vital concepts such as motivational methods, aspiration levels and self-evaluation have not attained significance and due place in practice. The concept of physical education and its programmes at various levels have to be restructured and modified according to the present conditions and needs so as to enable the modern child to enjoy the fullest possible benefits of physical education. Then only can it become a meaningful part of general education.

The present move is to establish physical education as a compact and complete academic subject which can magnificently kindle the spark and bring out the hidden talents and aspirations in a consecutive constructive manner. At present, physical educators have resolved to change the age-old concept of physical education as it was considered to be the one-hour-evening programme.

In other words, it is nothing but one-period physical exercises or events. In reality, it is not so. It has hot a tremendous role to play at school, college and university levels. The potentialities and idealistic virtues of men should be spotted out and exploited to the maximum or else the aims and objectives of education and physical education are totally defeated.

Moreover, the physical educators should not be content with their professional services in the educational institutions, if they fail to contribute to the actual development of personalities at their disposal. It is a period of transition for both education and physical education. They have to cope with the new changes and satisfy the pressing demands. They should unhesitatingly adopt newly discovered ways and means in their approaches to shape the personality of a growing child. Then they can deliver the goods in a fitting manner.

Today the world is highly competitive in nature. Physical education is no exception. It goes without saying that the programmes of physical education should be restyled and tailored to suit the present conditions in the educational institutions. Unless every facet of academic discipline is given the right place, education cannot but be a dismal failure.

Physical education promotes the whole being of man namely the body, mind and spirit to suitable and necessary highest level. So, it is to make physical education an academic discipline. Invariably all the physical educators are giving a clarion call for standardising the academic status of physical education. They try all out means to make it a full-fledged academic discipline.

Unfortunately various efforts like well intended seminars, etc., have not helped in getting physical education a respectable status in educational institution. It has been deprived of its legitimate, right and was made to have a secluded existence for name's sake, which did not create high esteem among physical educators themselves.

Conversely, they were more likely to develop an inferiority complex. The physical educators were openly branded and treated as second rate persons compared to the classroom teachers. The prime work to be undertaken is to make them feel strongly that physical education is on par with other branches and faculties of knowledge. They should have the necessary conviction on this point.

Unless physical education marches majestically along with other disciplines, the realisation of the goals of education in the true sense is impossible. A dynamic masterplan should be evolved to rearrange the course of action for making physical education an effective medium to achieve the desired ends of general education. The following suggestion may bring about good results.

SUGGESTED MASTER PLAN FOR PHYSICAL EDUCATION

a. The aims and objectives of physical education should be defined in clear-cut terms.

b. The close-knit relationship of physical education with other disciplines should be understood and established in an appropriate way so as to obtain the maximum benefits.

c. The concept and utility of movement patterns which form the basis of all types of labour and managerial affairs should be rightly appreciated.

d. Different bodies and individuals should be amalgamated to make united effort to achieve the full-fledged academic status for physical education.

e. It is of prime importance that experts and stalwarts from other fields are requested to put their heads and hearts together to make a better design for physical education by making them participate in lectures, seminars and workshops.

f. Short refresher courses may be held for physical educators to raise the standard of physical education as well as maximise their contribution to the field.

g. The various quarters should be convinced of the importance and need of physical education so that they will whole heartedly patronise the steps that the physical educators undertake. The governments at the centre and states should give priority to the physical educators in the matters of employment.

Physical education is a unique field where there are ample opportunities for demonstration of action and strict observance of rules. It is not to be found in other disciplines. The importance of "self" is stressed emphatically though the ultimate goal is to inculcate the feelings of group-spirit, group-interaction and group-welfare and service before self.

This is, no doubt, a special feature of physical education. The potentialities and scope of physical education are tremendous and they should be realised, and the conceptual framework and foundation should also be rationalized to pave the way for a renaissance in physical education. It is possible only through reformulating the theoretical perspective.

Physical education grows naturally, provided it has a strong academic status which helps in fear and fuller growth. Apart from this, status help to bring about an intellectual harmony, understanding and cooperation between the various personalities, agencies and associations involved in this field.

This naturally facilitates the evolution of a sound and practicable theory for the purpose of learning these activities effectively. Educational objectives are carefully planned in such a way as to inculcate social, moral and holistic virtues in the minds of young children, thereby making them fit personalities in this complicated and competitive world. Education as well as physical education plays a vital role to achieve this unique ambition.

No doubt, in modern life, parents cannot always afford to spare sufficient attention towards educating the young ones. The teachers are also not in a position to do justice as there is limited time at their disposal. Even if the teachers are prepared to render dedicate their selfless service to educate the students in a special and better manner, the students are not only unreceptive but they look down upon both the physical education teachers and the entire programme as it does not enjoy a reputation like other subjects.

The students also do not consider physical education as part of general education. These programmes are distinctly and decidedly alienated from the mainstream of education as they have been eternally branded, in practice, as the optional and extra evening hour programmes which have no value and significance in the academic, social and professional spheres.

Physical education has unfortunately lost its significance as it is not a subject for examination and graduation in the strictest sense. Invariably, the students, the society and even the teaching community give it stepmotherly treatment and less importance in curriculums at all levels. Everybody is privileged and entitled to choose his or her own branch of knowledge and pursue for personal and social betterment.

Educational institutions which have the moral and legal duty to cater to the genuine needs of the growing students according to their capacity and capability and resources and aspirations neither provide adequate facilities, amenities, and congenial atmosphere for young ones to take up a sporting career, nor regularise the time meant for physical education programmes. In this aspect, we have utterly disappointed the students of our days and they have been deprived of the privilege of enjoying the benefits of physical education.

The result is that they do not flock with enthusiasm to the fields nor do they stick to physical education activities for a long time. We cannot blame the students for their lack of ability or interest. The underlying reason for this is the present status of physical education. There is a great need therefore, to put physical education or par with other subjects.

2

FUNCTIONS OF PHYSICAL EDUCATION

PHYSICAL EDUCATION AND THE TASKS OF THE BODY

Even before the human embryo is as large as a fingernail, a tube has formed within it, enlarged at a certain point, and begun to pulsate. Thus the human heart has its beginning. It develops into a four-chambered organ which circulates the life blood for 80 years, without a stop in the pulsations which commenced in that tiny tube.

This is one of the tasks of the body–to develop and maintain an organ which is necessary to life. The body does this all unconsciously, and in the right timing and placing with respect to the other body organs.

In addition to the internal and unconscious tasks, the body also accomplishes a series of visible tasks of which a person is more conscious and which affect his feelings about himself as well as the attitudes of others toward him. These visible tasks of the body constitute the process, in part, of growing up and growing through the life cycle.

Consider, for example, the tasks of learning to walk. Sometimes between the ages of nine and fifteen months the bones, muscles and nerves of the legs and trunk have developed to the point where they are equal to the task of walking. Then the infant learns to walk with varying amounts of help and stimulation from other people. This task is followed by those of running, jumping and skipping.

The child learns to walk almost unconsciously. But even at this early level the gives evidence of being pleased with himself at this accomplishment, and he certainly experience the approval of others as he masters this task. From this time on, the tasks of the body are accomplished with a growing awareness and interest in them by the individual.

Although the body continues in its silent and organic way to accomplish the tasks of growth, such as readying the eyes for the task of reading, and preparing the gonads for the task of reproduction, the result is visible to the individual and to the people around him and they pay a great deal of attention to it.

The child soon learns that he will be judged by what his body accomplishes, and so he tries to make it do well, and he makes the best of whatever it does. This is one of the lessons of life - that we are judged by our bodies and can improve them.

This is true all through life. It is true of the events which constitute puberty, and of the events which take place in men and women around the age of fifty. It is true of the bodily reading apparatus at the age of 6, as well as at the age of 45. It is true of sweet sixteen and of bitter sixty-six.

The human boys is never left alone to achieve its visible uncriticized, as presumably is the case among oysters, ants, and butterflies. Among these organisms it seems unlikely that there is any social expectation about how one's body should develop, and therefore the individual oyster, ant, or butterfly is not likely to feel either social stigma or social approval for the way he looks. But with humans there is always a social judgment.

A person is always judged by the way he looks, and he knows and feels this judgment. The extent to which a society judges people by their appearance varies from one society to another. The ancient Greeks were more conscious of their bodies perhaps than many others; but probably no society exceeds the present-day American in the emphasis it places on looks.

Therefore there are two aspects of physical development, both of which are important for the happiness of people. One, which we have been considering, is the development of the body as it is perceived and valued by other people. Society judges people, and gives them approval or disapproval, partly by the way they look.

The other aspect is that of health and performance. For obvious reasons it is desirable to have good health and for the body to perform acceptably the physical tasks expects of it.

One might easily say that good physical health and bodily performance are more important than having a physical appearance which pleases people, and in a sense this true; but a person who is out of fashion because he has a big nose, or a receding chin, or is very tall or very short or very fat may feel this as keenly as someone else who has chronic ill health. Both aspects are important to the happiness of people, and physical education may well be concerned with both aspects.

Education can do three things for a person in relation to the tasks of the body:

(1) Help a person to achieve these tasks through physical training, proper diet, cosmetics, and grooming.

(2) Help a person to understand and accept inevitable bodily disadvantages, and to correct them as far as possible through instruments to aid the body, and to correct as braces for teeth, and glasses for eyes.

(3) Help a person to prepare for bodily changes in the course of physical growth.

We shall illustrate these three functions of education in relation to the physical changes of adolescence, which is the period when the body is of greatest concern to people.

BODY TASKS OF ADOLESCENCE

The human body grows from childhood to adulthood with such dramatic changes that everyone is aware of them, both the adolescents experiencing the changes and the remainder of the society witnessing them. Those who observe the changes expect adolescents to behave in accordance with their physical appearance, even though this may belie their chronological age. An early maturing 14-year old girl will be treated by older girls and boys as their equal, and they will often say and do things to her which are beyond her understanding and experience. A 15-year old, slow-maturing boy will be treated as a child by his own age-mates and those slightly older.

Most people remember their own adolescence with pleasure or discomfort depending on how well their own bodies met the expectations of the social group. Counsellors and medical practitioners report the concerns of boys and girls with their physical maturation and their physical appearance.

The fear that boys have of physical inadequacy is attested by many studies of adolescent personality difficulties. For instance, Schonfeld reported on the developmental and psychiatric evaluation of 258 boys aged 9 to 16 who presented personality difficulties and emotional conflicts associated with fears of physical inadequacy. He says that during the early part of the second decade of life personality conflicts and psychosomatic complaints may result from an apparent or actual delay in the age of onset of sexual maturation, or inadequacy of masculine development.

A recent questionnaire study of high schools students in confirms the prevalence of adolescent concerns with physique, both with the timing of maturation and with specific physical blemishes. Boys were concerned over being short, girls over being tall. Girls were concerned over having to wear glasses, with freckles and size of their noses, while both sexes were concerned over acne.

Physical appearance was a source of embarrassment to two girls, for different reasons.

During the junior high and high school days, the student was extremely sensitive about his physical appearance. He was short and stocky and awkward. He wore glasses, and acne, and wore braces on my teeth. He was particularly self-conscious about my rather prominent nose. Two of the boys in junior high school indulged in teasing me about my nose and as a result he was very miserable during that period. He withdrew from his companions and had only a few friends. He spent a great deal of time in the library reading books which were usually of an adult level. He compensated, also, by studying hard and standing at the top of my class scholastically. His feelings of inferiority in so far as my physical appearance was concerned never quite left me, although he developed into a person who was average physically, and he realize that he no longer stand out as different from most people.

The physical changes accompanying adolescence were a source of constantly painful embarrassment to him. He was much fatter than anyone else in my group. He was mortified by the development of my breasts, which were very large. Menarche, while accompanied by no physical discomfort, seemed so disgusting to him that he tried desperately to conceal the fact of menstruation from everyone, even his mother. He was as ashamed of it as if it had been syphilis. His coming of age was a period of intense unhappiness.

As one becomes aware of the difficulties that some boys and girls have in adolescence of accepting their bodies and making the most of them, one sees how physical education might help them, through preparing them for the bodily changes of puberty, through helping them to understand and accept certain inevitable disadvantages, and through helping them to achieve the physical skills that are valued in adolescence and to make the most of their physical appearance through grooming and cosmetics. Specifically, there are three things which every high school department of physical education might do.

In biology or hygiene, teach about the physical changes of adolescence, stressing the normality of variability. This has not yet been done to any appreciable extent. Yet this kind of knowledge would set at rest the worries about their normality of all boys and girls except the few who have serious emotional disturbances.

Make it easy for a student to ask for information and assurance with respect to his own physical development. Every school and college should have someone who is easily approached and who is prepared by personality and by training to discuss with students their concerns about their physical development. This person will usually be a doctor, a nurse, a teacher of biology or physical education.

THIS STATE OF THE BODY IS ONLY ONE OF THE IMPORTANT FACTORS

The foregoing discussion might be interpreted by the unwary reader to support the proposition that the body takes priority; that the way it accomplishes its growth tasks determines the social and emotional functioning of the adolescent. There is no question that a tendency in this direction does exist —a tendency expressed by a correlation coefficient that is reliably positive, but not very high. But there are many individual exceptions to such as general proposition, as was pointed out by More in his study of the relations of the physical to other aspects of development in adolescence. He found a number of early-maturing boys and girls who were not particularly early in their social development, even though the general rule was for early maturity to be associated with early social and emotional maturity. This tendency he found more pronounced in girls than in boys. The reason for the low order of relationship between physical, social and emotional aspects of maturity in adolescence is probably partly that the social and emotional qualities of a person are established by middle childhood and tend to carry over through adolescence, so that a child with an easy social personality and a stable emotionality moves through adolescence with these qualities regardless of how his body matures unless it is drastically deviant.

Partly, also, the reason for the relatively low relationship of the physical to the social and emotional aspects of living in adolescence is that teachers and counsellors and parents have been relatively successful in helping boys and girls to accept their bodies and thus to adjust to physical deviations within the fairly wide range that can be called normal.

This discussion raises the question of maturation versus learning, or heredity versus environment. Physical education theory must be continually responding to our knowledge and our biases on the topic of the relative significance of heredity or environment in shaping a person's life. Heredity held sway until the early of the 20th century, and then gave way to environmentalism which must have required a major reorientation of physical education theory.

Now there appears to be something of a swing of the pendulum away from environmentalism though it does not approach the hereditarism of 50 years ago. Physical educators are in a good situation to draw usefully and impartially from the growing knowledge and genetic and constitutional factors in human development as well as from the growing knowledge of the effects of the family and the peer group and the educational environment on the person.

BODY TASKS AT OTHER AGE LEVELS

The tasks of the body have their special forms at the several age periods, and consequently the functions of health and physical education should be carried out differently in the different age periods. There is something important to be done through education, however, in relation to the body tasks at all ages from 6 to the last years of life.

Middle Childhood, 6-12

During middle childhood our society sets two major for children which involves their bodies.

One is the task of learning the physical skills that are necessary for the games and physical activities of childhood-such skills as throwing and catching, kicking, tumbling, swimming and handling simple tools. The body prepares to accomplish these tasks through growth of bone and muscle, but they have to be learned, and they are learned partly from the peer group and partly through school. Boys are expected to do a better job of learning these skills than girls.

The other task in to learn wholesome attitudes and habits concerning the care of the body, which give a sense of physical normality and adequacy, the ability to enjoy using the body, and a wholesome attitude toward sex.

Early Adulthood, 20-40

In early adulthood the sexes differ most widely in their bodily tasks, because at this time the female task of child-bearing takes priority over the other feminine tasks for most women. To perform this task well, both mentally and physically, a woman needs a variety of kinds of preparation, some of which can only come through health and physical education. It is not claimed here that preparation for the physical act of motherhood should be a part of high school or college education, though some interesting educational experiments have been made in this direction. Rather, this preparation is most likely to come in early adulthood through the informal means of coaching by one's mother and doctor and by reading, or through the more formal means of classes for expectant mothers maintained by adult education agencies. The preparation takes the form of exercises before and after childbirth, of diet, and of learning the pros and cons of nursing a child.

For both sexes there is the everyday but all-important task of learning to use the body wisely and effectively-to conserve one's energy and maintain one's health during the physical prime of life. This is the time when women and men can look their best, and when their success and satisfaction in life is dependent in a major way on their making the best of their bodies.

Middle Age, 40-60

In middle age there is a fundamental task of accepting and adjusting to the physiological changes that characterize this period. Aging of the body tissues has been going on, mostly unnoticed, since early adulthood. Muscular strength has been diminishing, neuromuscular skills have been fading, and the body has been slowing down. Some of the physical symptoms of aging are:

Growth of stiff hair in the nose, ears, and eyelashes of men.

Growth of hair on the upper lip of women.

Drying and wrinkling of the skin.

Deposition of fat around the middle.

Presbyopia-loss of accommodative power of the lens of the eye. The elasticity of the lens decreases steadily from childhood to old age, and by the age of seventy-five the lens is ordinarily completely inelastic, making it impossible for the eye to adjust itself unaided to the task of focusing on objects at varying distances.

The menopause, or climacterium, occurs in women over a period of several years, usually between forty-five and fifty-five. Menstruation gradually ceases and the ovaries become mere masses of connective tissue. With the cessation of ovarian activity, the delicate balance of the endocrine system is disturbed. Physical symptoms may take the form of hot and cold flashes, dizziness, sweating, insomnia, and excitability.

Thus the body accomplishes its natural task of growing older, but this tends to create real problems of adjustment as great or greater than those of adolescence. The exercise habits of men sometimes have to be çhanges. There are profound effects on the sexual activities and interests of men and women. A minority of people suffer from more or less severe psychological depression associated with physiological changes.

Women and men can make this period of life much more comfortable for themselves by understanding what is taking place in their bodies, by using various devices to keep their physical abilities up to earlier levels and to defend themselves against the attacks of physical middle-aging. For instance, it is a definite fact that a great many people at about age 50 cease to read more than a few minutes a day because "their eyes hurt", when a suitable adjustment of reading glasses or bifocals would clear up the trouble.

A most valuable kind of adult education is given through books, lectures, and classes on the conservation of personal physical resources in middle age.

Later Maturity, 60+

The slow downward trend of physical vigour and physical beauty which starts in middle age continues in the years of later maturity, sometimes just as slowly, and sometimes more swiftly. Most people maintain very good health and vigour well past the age of 70. Still, the body is aging, but the rate of aging varies enormously among individuals, and it seems likely that medical science will soon find ways to control and decrease the rate of aging in those people who now age most rapidly. The characteristic illnesses of later maturity-cancer, heart disease, and arthritis- are coming gradually under some degree of medical control

No doubt people can aid their bodies to perform more effectively in later maturity by paying attention to their diet, to exercise, to grooming, and to the doctor's advice. An important part of any program of counselling or group study in preparation for retirement should be some lessons on the maintenance of heath.

Conclusion

This we see that throughout the life cycle the body has its tasks to perform, appropriate tasks to each stage of life. The body has its own wisdom, but it can be aided by the kind of wisdom which we get from medical science.

The person has a great stake in how well his body performs its tasks, and he can help his body do better, given the kind of information and training which modern health and physical education provide. However, all people will have to accept the fact that their bodies are not performing as well as they would like, or that their physical appearance is not as good as they would like to be. To some this comes early in life-to all it comes eventually. They can be helped by physical education to accept these unfavourable facts, and to do their best in the face of these facts.

The tasks of the body are especially important to personal wellbeing in the present-day American society, because out society sets such great store on the physical appearance of people. Possibly there will be less emphasis on sheer looks as time goes on, and as the proportion of older people in the society increases. But there is not likely to be any decrease in the social emphasis on health, and people will be expected more and more to make the most of their bodies. Perhaps there will develop a public opinion which blames people for their own ill health, as Samuel Butler suggested in Erewhon. In his Utopia Butler said that people might be severely censured if they became ill, because they were expected to know how to keep healthy, and illness could only come through gross negligence.

In any case it appears that the tasks of the body will be better performed at all ages if people accept the help of health and physical education, and if this profession does what appears to be its manifest duty.

3

PRINCIPLES OR FOUNDATIONS OF PHYSICAL EDUCATION

RAISON D'ETRE

Beginning with some sort of physical activities in the past-unsympathetic and unorganized physical education today has developed into an academic discipline with a sound 'body of knowledge.' It has also grown into a profession which draws its technical tenets from a variety of professional and scientific fields on the one hand, and code of ethics from social sciences on the other.

The academician and the professional in the physical educator have to understand the foundations of the policies, practices and programmes of physical education. Precisely, foundations of a discipline are made of fundamental beliefs and convocations which have been verified. Facts and only facts are the building blocks of beliefs and convictions. Research is the main instrument through which facts are known and theories formulated.

Theories, in turn, are subjected to more rigorous research so that they could be verified in order to take the shape of laws or principles. Theories are modified in the light of new facts or observations which can explain a phenomenon more rationally and logically. The search for truth—the ultimate reality - is an arduous job. It requires the use of scientific method which deftly blends two great epistemological approaches, empiricism and rationalism.

In simple words, we can learn about the universe of ideas, objects or phenomena by using our powers of observation. We can try to understand what these observations mean by using our power of reason, and test our reasoning power against a new set of observations.

The application of scientific method to the study of 'man and movement' in the modern era has resulted in tremendous amount of knowledge. The sciences of 'life, matter and mind' and humanities have contributed 'facts' hitherto unknown to the physical educators. The scientists and scholars working under these fields are not directly concerned with physical education and sport. Their approach, therefore, is fragmentary. The emergence of specialities and sub-specialities of various branches of knowledge such as sport-medicine, sport physiology, sport psychology, sport sociology, bio-mechanics etc. as an interface between physical education and pure sciences has brought physical education to the brink of a unique discipline the roots of which lie in the science laboratories and boughs and branches on the play fields.

The facts received from various sort bio-sciences and art disciplines are to be synthesized and made applicable to the process of building of an enduring edifice of principles which should serve as a guiding light for practices to physical educators alone. It is their prerogative to justify their policies on the basis of scientific principles on the one hand and social value-system on the other.

PRINCIPLES: DEFINITION AND SOURCES

The word principle is defined as "a fundamental truth, a law, a promotive force, a general law or rule as a guide to action." A tentatively organized body of facts is generally called a theory. When verified, either through personal experience or experimentation, a theory takes the shape of a principle. So principles are basic beliefs or fundamental truths which guide and direct actions. A philosophical belief may be relative or absolute in terms of its validity with reference to time and place but a scientific principle is characterized by its universality and a sort of permanence. One of the important things about principles is that they have a universal appeal and mass following.

Physical education is a unique field. In comparison to other fields, it stands apart for its multi-faced form. In one way physical education is an art, in another it is a science, yet in another way it is an organized activity programme so essential for human growth and development. The origin of physical education is traced to the information coming from a wide variety of art and science disciplines. Barrow believes that principles of physical education are chiefly derived from (i) basic sciences (ii) humanities and (iii) social heritage of man. Their virtue lies in the fact that they are founded on human nature, and insight, experience and understanding. The three sources of principles are interrelated. The categorization is simply a matter or convenience rather than rule because whatever man believes or knows to be true is the result of interplay of internal and external forces. In other to have a better understanding of the principles, let us classify them into (i) philosophical beliefs, and (ii) scientific principles.

Philosophy is principally reflective and contemplative in nature. Therefore, philosophical beliefs are the result of 'human observation, experience, understanding and insight'—both personal and collective. The individual and society cannot exist without each other. The personal philosophy and social philosophy influence each other. The personal philosophy and social society cannot exist without each other. The personal philosophy and social philosophy influence each other and direct human thought and action. Powerful beliefs of the "big brains" of a culture often become part of the social philosophy.

Ordinary thoughts and beliefs are good enough for individual consumption i.e. to regulate the day to day behaviour. Philosophic beliefs held by intellectual giants life Aristotle, Plato, Socrates, Chanakya, Manu, Patanjali,

Gemini and a host of others have guided human society through the centuries. However, a large number of these philosophic beliefs have become invalid and lost their sanctity in the light of more reliable observations and innovations. Philosophic beliefs are considered tentative in the sense that change with the time flux. What was considered true and right centuries ago, may not fit into the overall scheme of things today. Paradoxically, they are dynamic and progressive on the one hand, they are rigid and dogmatic on the other because they draw their strength and sanctity from customs, traditions, social and religious taboos. Customs and traditions are hard to change because they have mass-following.

A philosopher may be very rational in his outlook, a commoner invariably is more sentimental in his approach to life. That, perhaps, is the reason why the common man holds fast to the philosophic beliefs handed over to him as a part of social fast to the philosophic beliefs handed over to him as a part of social legacy and cultural heritage.

In some ways, the truth is fundamental even though its interpretation may change from time to time and situation to situation, in other ways, the truth is relative i.e. what is true for one may not be true for another. So is man's faith in the philosophic beliefs. The changing face of the world on account of scientific discoveries and inventions, socio-economic upheavals, urbanization and industrialization, is bringing about catastrophic changes in the well-established values of life and well-entrenched philosophic beliefs. Contemporary political, social, economic, religious philosophies have attained a new meaning. So much is the impact of change on our life that we find every new generation coming out with new ideas and beliefs about life and social, economic and religious systems. Education as well as physical education cannot remain unaffected in this fast-changing environs and ideas.

Scientific principles are those generalizations the validity and reliability of which have been proved through empirical and/or experimental techniques. Although scientists, in general, don't consider scientific beliefs to be unchangeable, their faith in well-established principles is absolute. Law of Gravitation, Newton's laws of Motion, Archimede's principles etc. are irrefutable principles because they are the result of unchallengeable scientific evidence. They will change only when more substantial and enduring facts are known about the phenomena which these principles govern. Except for a few "missing links, " a large number of sciences of life and matter have developed to such an extent that the possibility of replacing the hitherto gathered knowledge with new facts is simply remote.

The sciences of behaviour and mind are still caught in the web of theories. There is more than adequate scope for many hypotheses to be tested and verified in subjects like psychology, motor behaviour etc. More precise methodologies and refined techniques are required to fill gaps in knowledge in the field of science. The emergence of sport-specific sciences like exercise and sport physiology, sport psychology, bio-mechanics, kinesiology etc. is a step in the right direction. The sport scientists are trying hard to close the gaps between scientific facts about human movement and the methodologies which govern the process of training. The scientific principles bring physical educators much closer to the realities.

The worth of physical education lies in its reliance on the principles—both philosophic and scientific. Williams argues that "one difference between a profession and a trade is that the former is guided by principles based upon scientific facts and/or philosophical concepts while a trade is guided only by rules, methods and directions. The main characteristic of a profession is its reliance upon facts of nature and/or philosophy as the basis for determination of procedure." While philosophic beliefs help the physical educators to formulate aim, objectives and goals of physical education on the basis of values which the individual and society cherish, the scientific principles give him an insight into the realities which govern processes, procedures, methods and methodologies of professional practices.

NEED OF PRINCIPLES IN PHYSICAL EDUCATION

Principles serve numerous purposes in physical education:

1. They form the foundations of physical education as an academic discipline. The entire edifice of activity programme is constructed on the bedrock of principles. Principles provide strength to physical education to stand on its own legs and justify its academic policies and practices.
2. They assist the physical educators to set realistic objectives and goals as well as justify the means to achieve the ends. Professional practices based on solid scientific principles and firm convictions are difficult to challenge.
3. Principles make physical education a socially relevant endeavour, and the physical educators earn a respectable status in the academe as well as in the society. The greater the reliance on principles, the higher the status for the physical educator.
4. Principles provide authority to the physical educators to challenge those administrative directives which go against professional ethics, interests of the participants in physical activity programmes, and well-established universal practices.
5. They serve as guidelines for planning and construction of curricula and course-content for various physical education course, and set criteria for their evaluation from time to time.

4

BIOLOGICAL FOUNDATIONS OF PHYSICAL EDUCATION

INTRODUCTION

Biological sciences deal with life and life-processes. Microbiology, zoology, botany, anthropology, anatomy and physiology are a few disciplines and sub-disciplines of biological sciences. Through sustained observation, rational thinking and empirical evidence biologists have been able to explode myths about origin and propagation of life on the Earth. The 'story of life' makes an interesting reading but it has been an uphill task for the biologists to construct this story from the 'mute' and fragmentary evidence recorded in fossils, rocks, cases etc.

Moreover, the evidence is so much scattered in terms of time and space that it leaves many vital questions about life unanswered. This gap in knowledge is generally filled with theoretical explanations. That, perhaps, is the reason why the history of life is still perforated.

Since in physical education, our direct concern is man and his movement, the focus of discussion, in this chapter, would be those biological facts which have relevance to the understanding of the biological nature of man and its bearing on physical activity programmes.

To begin with, it has more or less, been accepted that man was not dropped from Heaven but is a product of biological evolution which spanned our billions of years. In the beginning, there existed the cosmic matter on the earth. After a long period, the inorganic material dramatically became organic and laid the foundation for "a new order".

About two thousand million years ago life evolved out of the organic matter and manifested itself in the form of protozoa. Catastrophic environmental changes went on the earth for hundreds of millions of years as a consequence of which more complex organisms evolved. Invertebrates that are said to have appeared on the science some five hundred million years ago, were simply unicellular organisms. From unicellular to multi-cellular, organism to prosimilar, to humanoids, to home spines etc., life evolved in stages.

The apeman, the cave man and the civilized man are links in the biological evolution as well as cultural revolution. Approximately, five hundred thousand years ago evolved the 'intelligent man' and there from began the story of civilization and culture. For a considerably long period of time did man remain slave to natural forces and adapted himself to the changing understand the forces of nature and make the environment conducive for his living.

Interaction between man and his environment was instrumental in the development of man's mental faculties. The nett result of this phenomenal change was that in the 'struggle for existence' man began to rely more on his brain than the 'brawn' which gave him an edge over other animals.

Biologists are of the considered opinion that the major factors which assisted the transition from ape to man were (1) natural selection (2) mitosis—the reproduction of cells through cell-division, (3) meiosis of the sex cell or sexual selection, (4) use and disuse of organs, (5) environmental changes, and (6) other correlative factors/changes. Biologists are also unanimous in accepting the hypothesis of 'Survival to the Fittest'. It lays down that animals and animal-species which could not brave the onslaughts of the changing environment or catastrophic occurrences such as scarcity of food, endemics, climatic upheavals etc. could not survive and became extinct. Those that were "fit" and adapted themselves to the sudden of gradual changes could continue to live. Genetic variations and transmission of traits are also explained on the basis of this widely accepted principle.

Connecting the loose ends of the biological story of man's development, Darwin emphasized: " In the course of evolution, man's ancestors lost certain characteristics either fully or in part; a keen sense of smell, the hairy covering on the body, the majority of the dermal muscles, the tail, prehensile feet, pointed aerobes etc." In discussing the causes that led man to adopt erect mode of locomotion, he assumed that "change of feeding" was of great importance. That occurred when hominoids began spending more and more time in "search of food." Genetic variation and environmental changes are cited as the chief agents causing the development of 'modern man'.

Even though no perceptible change seems to have occurred to man in the last thirty-thousand years the evolutionary process has been going on uninterruptedly like an under—current. Biologically all human beings have similar physical characteristics, racial variations are due to geographical and ecological factors.

Upright body posture and adoption of erect mode of locomotion are considered significant stepping stones in the ascent of man to the apex of biological hierarchy. Revolutionary as these changes proved, they led to the freedom of of re-limbs and development of cerebrum in man. When the arms became free they developed greater mobility and enabled man to perform variety of bodily movements such as hanging, throwing, hitting, carrying things from one place to another etc. As a quadruped man used mouth, like other animals, to carry objects and also fight the opponent (s). The freedom of mouth is said to become responsible for development of language in the human race.

Consequently, man had a number of advantages over other animals. He could protect himself better from animal attacks and natural calamities and procure food more conveniently. He had enough time to 'think' and attend to other things. With the greater mobility of limbs and versatility of 'mind' man laid the foundation for a sort of civilization- the civilization of the primitive man. The accidental or international discovery of fire, wheel, axe, hammer and the like brought about highly significant changes in man's life style and initiated cultural revolution.

The biological evolution and sociocultural revolution have mixed up so well that it has become difficult to discuss on aspect of life on the Earth without reference to other(s). Evolution and revolution have proved a blessing and a bane at the same time. They created the new and destroyed the old. They will create something newer to destroy what is today new.

After having developed a keen intellect and intelligence man began to change the environment with urbanization and industrialization. He left his natural habitat which required to make use of body and its powers. The changed environment - his own creation - forced him to rely too much on his mental powers and machines, and neglect the body that had helped him weather a thousand storms since origin of life. Undoubtedly, man is the master of his destiny because he has numerous techniques and methodologies at his command to combat and tame the forces of nature and lives life the way he likes. On the other hand, it is undeniable fact that both biologic evolution and cultural revolution have brought about certain weaknesses in the human body and its working system as a result of which man looks inferior to animals in many respects although he is far superior to them in intelligence:

Some of these biological weaknesses are listed below:-

1. The physical fitness level in man is now considerably lower than what it was in the past.

2. With the invention of tools, man's manual skills i.e., combative dexterity, sensing danger etc. have been pushed back.

3. The rate of incidence of hypo-kinetic diseases has gone up beyond measure. Heart diseases, despite best medical care, are on the ascendance.

4. Pursuit of materialistic philosophy has added to the woes of man. Constantly increasing stresses and strains on human mind have become an instrument of psycho-somatic disorders.

5. Posture and body mechanics have been adversely affected due to the changes human anatomy underwent during evolution.

6. Man has fallen victim to malnutrition. The rich and the poor suffer from it alike. There is artificiality in producing and consuming food.

With this 'weak' biologic legacy and accelerating mechanization of life, it would be difficult for the mankind to live a qualitative life and survive for long. Great damage has already been done to the human body and the Earth's ecology. The tide of deterioration—whether in health and fitness or in environment—has to be stemmed. The only silver lining in the cloud is the 'right education' which, at this crucial juncture, must consist of understanding and following, in letter and spirit, the principles of physical activity, fitness and health. This is the greatest need of the hour for 'the brave new world'.

PHYSICAL ACTIVITY : BASIS OF LIFE

All living beings are naturally active :they move and they live: they live because they move. Life is characterized by movement. Even the plants which seem obviously inert, also move. All functions of the organism depend upon movement. Movement is the cosmic principle of matter and mind. The inherent energy in the matter generates movement and movement, in turn, generates and sustains life. Each atom of the universe and each cell of the organism are blessed with vital energy which causes them 'move'.

From the moment of conception i.e., fertilization of the female egg by the sperm, to death life is nothing but an endless series of movement. The process of reproduction-fertilization, cell division, cell-multiplication, cell-differentiation, birth of a new organism - is based on movement. Movement is an inborn quality of the organism. When movement ceases, life ceases to exist.

The biologists assert that activity—whether survival or developmental—is a part and parcel of man's biological inheritance. In the primitive past, activity helped man to survive, in the modern day world it assists him to live vigorously and enjoy the blessings of Nature and fruit of his endeavours. Play, games, sports etc. are legacy of the past and justify physical activity as the basis for a qualitative life.

EXERCISE : A DAILY NECESSITY

Not only is physical activity a basic organic necessity, it is a daily requirement. Like food, it must be taken every day. Preponderance of scientific evidence indicates that walking, jogging, playing vigorous games and sports and manual work stimulate growth, processes, and keep the individual physically fit. Williams points out that "all life functions depend upon physical fitness, and greater the physical fitness, the greater the potential life efficiency."

A golden principle of health and fitness is regular physical activity. In general, physical activity improves body posture and strengthens musculature. It causes better digestion, efficient elimination of toxins and other waste products, greater vascularization, stabilized respiration, and greater output of energy. It needs to be emphasized that the real benefits from physical activity are derived only when regularity is strictly observed and the activity to be engaged in calls for a supreme effort. Bortz observed, "There is no drug in current or perspective use that holds as much for sustained health as a life time program of physical exercise."

The human body consists of billions of tiny cells of different types such as muscular cells, skeletal cells, cardiac cells, smooth-muscle cells, nerve cells etc. The cells are not only building blocks of the body , they are also "store-house of energy." These cells perform all vital life functions like digestion, elimination of waste products etc. Regular physical activity stimulates them to perform their respective "duties" at the optimal level thereby enhancing the individual's capacity to work more efficiently and for a longer time. The regular exercisers are significantly healthier and fitter than non-exercisers. The researchers feels that "....if we maintain adequate levels of muscular strength, endurance, flexibility, heart-lung efficiency, balance, bone integrity, and nervous system function, we can retain good performance levels to meet the physical and mental demands required for independent living, well into the chronological 80s and 90s."

From infancy to old age, all human beings perform daily chores, and attend to routines. All the involves physical activity, its quantity and quality being dependent on age, sex, vocation, profession etc. This routine physical activity is hopelessly inadequate to maintain a high degree of health and fitness because the systems of the body are not goaded and geared to work at a higher level of load. Besides this, the modern lifestyle is a paradox in itself. On the one hand, it is sedentary, on the other it is plagued by hurrying-surrying. The routine physical activity is not "exercise" in the real sense of the term. It is simply coping with the necessities of life.

The qualitative exercise is one which is done for its own sake and performed in a tension-free atmosphere. A balanced exercise and activity programme must necessarily include five components viz., (i) Relaxation movements for they help reduce stress and tension, (ii) Endurance exercises which stimulate cardio-respiratory processes, (iii) Muscle-strengthening exercises that provide force for movement, (iv) Stretching exercise which enhance joint mobility, and (v) Balance exercises which reduce the risk of falling and injury.

BENEFITS OF PHYSICAL EXERCISE

Anatomic, physiological and psychological benefits of the large-muscle activity are numerous. *First,* physical activity performed in accordance with the laws of bio-mechanics, helps in developing a correct posture and maintaining it. Sitting, standing, sleeping, walking and running postures are extremely important in life for they allow us to economise on energy and add to the aesthetic value. People with pastoral deviations become a laughing stock and feel inferior in the presence of others, thus aggravating their miseries.

Second, repeated powerful contraction of the skeletal muscles causes increase in their girth, size and efficiency. When a muscle fibre is stimulated, it produces the maximal tension or none at all; the higher the frequency, the greater the tension and also greater the rate at which tension can be developed.

Endurance of the neuro-muscular system is closely related to the ability of a muscle to maintain tension when its is repeatedly stimulated. Through exercise, muscles develop greater contracting ability, strength, capacity for energy storage, endurance and beautiful shape.

Third, the powerful exercise causes chemical change in the muscle i.e., increase in phosphorescent content, glycogen, non-nitrogenous substances and haemoglobin. The nerve impulse travels more rapidly across the motor-end plate in the muscle fibre due to which reaction time improves.

Fourth, through muscular exercise, the cardiac muscle becomes stronger so as the contract more powerfully to push out more blood to the arteries. The heart which is about the size of man's closed fist is the finest pump ever known. In an average adult, it beats 40 million times a year, and more than 2.8 billion times in a life time. It pumps 4,300 gallons of blood daily through 60,000 miles of blood vessels.

Precisely, a normal heart pumps out 10.2 litres of blood a minute in normal conditions while a trained "athletic heart" pumps out 22 litres. The athletic heart is so muscular that it can pump the same amount of blood with 50 beats per minute the average heart pumps with 75 beat per minute. Thus, the athletic heart will beat 13 million fewer times per year. It works less, rests more, and consequently takes a much times per year. It works less, rests more, and consequently takes a much longer time to wear out.

Fifth, physical exercise enlarges all the coronary arteries which feed the heart. It increases collateral circulation so that more than one blood vessel will supply a given area of the heart. Physiologists observes: "Exercise could open up the blood vessels supplying the heart making them less liable to obstruction, and where a partial blockade has developed, vigorous effort could encourage the development of new alternative pathways for the blood." This will prevent the possibility of a heart attack. It lowers the concentration of cholesterol in the blood vessels and fat in the blood.

Sixth, sustained physical activity not only lowers the blood pressure but also it teaches the heart how to extract oxygen from the blood more efficiently. The congestive heart appears large because the muscle is stretched with fluid. The athlete's heart is large because it is muscular. Pavo Nurmi who won nine gold medals in long distance running, had a muscular heart three times the normal size.

Seventh, physical activity causes numerical increase in the RBCs and WBCs thereby ensuring more efficient transportation of food and oxygen to various parts of the body and potentiating individual's ability to combat disease respectively. The greater capitalization, due to exercise, accelerates cell-metabolism and smoothens the road for sturdy growth of the cells.

Eighth, exercise helps regulate breathing. Accepting that the effect of strenuous exercise on respiratory functions is not very clear, researchers hypothesize that "the trained subject demonstrates (a) a decrease in the minute volume of breathing required for the performance of a given load, indicating an improvement required for the performance of a given load, indicating an improvement in the efficiency of ventilation, (b) an increase in maximal respiratory minute volume that can be achieved during very strenuous exertion.

It is probable that the respiratory superiority of the athlete lies not so much in a large vital capacity as in a greater ability to utilize his maximal lung capacity... when exertion is severe, both the minute volume and the frequency of breathing may continue to increase throughout the period of work although there may be a slight decrease in the tidal volume......."

Finally, strenuous activity improves digestion and hastens evacuation process. Increased mobility in the intestinal tract may be due to the fact that exercise causes the body to release increased amount of magnesium into the intestinal tract. The transit time for most people is usually twelve to twenty four hours whereas the marathon runners find that a meal can pass through their systems in as little as four to six hours.

Individual psychological benefits of physical activity. Include: positive changes in self-perceptions and well-being, improvement in self-confidence and awareness, positive changes in mood, relief of tension, relief of feelings such as depression and anxiety, influence on premenstrual tension, increased mental well-being, increased alertness and clear thinking, increased energy and ability to cope with daily activity, increased enjoyment of exercise and social contacts, and the development of positive coping strategies.

GROWTH & DEVELOPMENT AND PHYSICAL ACTIVITY

Activity is the basis of growth and development. The faster the child moves, the faster it grows is an oft-quoted biological dictum. The entire process of reproduction—fertilization, cell-division, cell-multiplication, cell-differentiation—is based on innate biological activity. Functional changes accompany structural transformation and help the organism to adjust and adopt to the environment. Movement and growth processes are directly and closely related. It is impossible to think of one without the other.

Most animals are organically complete at birth. They acquire no appendages in life. However, they grow in stature and size. It is interesting that chronological advancement does not cause significant behavioural changes in animals. They continue to depend upon their instinctive urges and follow the dictates of nature for their survival. In the case of man, things are different. As the human child grows in years, he acquires knowledge and skills chiefly due to quantitative and qualitative changes in his physical structure. His behavioural patterns become more complex. He develops mentally too. Rather, his physical and mental growth curves move up concurrently.

The words growth and development are often used interchangeably. Putting aside the semantic debate, suffice to say that growth is only one aspect of development which is a life-long process. Precisely, growth is a concrete biological process in which the organism gains in size, volume, girth, height and weight. It underscores enlargement of cells, fibres, muscles, bones and organs day by day and year by year. Anatomically, growth is a quantitative change in structure and form observed and objectively measured over a time span. Development, on the other hand, is a much wider term indicating "advancement, more unfoldment, a progressive change—a sort of growing towards greater maturity" . It is a qualitative change in the structural, functional and behavioural aspects of the organism.

Growth is controlled and determined by genetic factors, development is dependent upon external factors such as nutrition, health care, physical activity etc. Benedick considers development to be a "process in which the internal physiological changes and the psychological processes stimulated by them are integrated in a way which enable the individual to master further and a new environmental stimulations". Growth reaches its peak by the time a boy or a girl crosses "teens" but development processes continue further. Growth mostly is physical while development covers also mental, intellectual, emotional and social aspects. Growth is objectively and directly measured; measurement of development is possible only through measured; measurement of development is possible only through indirect means. Growth is an orderly phenomenon characteristic of species: it involves structural changes. Though there are individual differences in growth pattern, various predefined periods of growth the common to all individuals of the same species. Development is characterized by inter-linked and interdependent processes of differentiation, integration and learning. Differentiation refers to cellular specialization and integration denotes co-ordination of various cellular systems.

Learning—a psycho-physiological phenomenon—underlines 'acquisition of new responses or modification of old responses as a result of experience or practice'. Chronological growth may be important in numerous ways e.g., deciding one's admission in school, categorization in minor or major under constitutional provision etc. From the viewpoint of curriculum planning in physical education and training for competitive sport, chronological growth is not a valid yardstick for knowing one's abilities, qualities and capabilities.

GENERAL PRINCIPLES GOVERNING GROWTH

The human growth is governed by several general principles, the knowledge of which helps teachers to plan academic as well as activity curriculum accordingly.

- The growth is a result of interaction between the germ-plasm and environment. The seed which is a gift of nature, contains all the essential characteristics which a child shall have by it is incapable of transforming itself into an adult in the absence of conducive environmental factors such as nutrition, air, water, protection, activity etc. It is all a matter of seed-soil relationship.
- The growth follows an orderly sequence. The development of structure and function is progressive. A simple-to-complex order is uniformly maintained through out. The growth is cephalo-caudal as well as proximo-distal, As astute progression is discernible in the acquisition of motor and mental skills. Every child, says Gessell, "sits before he stands; he babbles before he talks, he fabricates before he tells the truth: he draws a circle before he draws a square; he is selfish before he is altruistic ; he is dependent on others before he achieves dependence on self."
- The growth is a continuous but gradual process. From the stage of zygotic formation to adulthood, a child passes through well-demarcated periods of accelerated growth and consolidation alternately. However, various stages of growth fuse into one

another, thereby making the whole affair a single and smooth continuum. 'Sudden spurts' of growth emerge from the quieter and less dramatic periods. The developmental gains of one stage are carried on to the next stage without hurdle. It takes roughly eighteen long year for the human nonage to become an adult.

- The growth is a creative process. From conception to the completion of adolescence dramatic changes occur in the human organism anatomically, physiologically and behaviourally. The acquisition of new motor skills, habits, concepts, attitudes and the like is part of this creative process.

- The growth in some direction is inevitable. The zygote transforms itself into an embryo and foetus from an impulsion. Lack of ideal nutrition, oxygen and protection from disease may retard developmental processes but it hardly impedes growth.

- Different aspects of growth proceed at different rate to speed. The physical, mental, emotional, intellectual and social aspects of growth, though closely related, have different pace of movement. If children of the same age were compared on various parameters of growth, marked variations would be found. Some are early mutterer in one aspect but late mutterer in the other. It may be true in reverse order. Complete synchronization among all aspects of growth is a rare phenomenon.

- Each individual grows in his own unique way. Though the broad sequence of growth in the same in all individuals the rate of growth varies from individual to individual, depending upon genetic and environmental factors. To quote Gessell again "Some children are tall and some short, some slender others stocky; some are physically strong, others are weak;

some are intellectually keen others are dull. There are the energetic and the phlegmatic, the agile and the awkward, the courageous and the fearful, the outgoing and the in-going personality."

- Growth is affected by internal and external factors. What an individual receives from his parents, grandparents and fore-fathers is nurtured by the environment in which he is brought up. Heredity sets limits for development in terms of potential. No ideal environment can help the child transgress these limits.

- Anatomically, various organs of the body grow at different rate of speed. Each organ reaches its maximal dimension at a certain period of time. Even though this seems to be a chaos, geneticists have found some order in it. The feet, for instance, speed up first reaching their peak growth rate only after about three months after the adolescence spurt has begun. In another six months, it is the turn of the calf muscles and the thighs. Four months later the hips and chest begin to broaden at an accelerated speed, followed by shoulders, In both sexes, the length of the trunk and the depth of the chest reach peak growth last of al. In infancy and childhood, many children look disproportionate but with the passage of time, body dimensions settle down.

- Growth is characterized by fluctuation. The road to development is not smooth but undulated, Genetic and environment factors such as dietary habits, physical and mental stresses and strains, lack of parental and health care might cause fluctuation in growth. The fluctuation is neither a drawback nor disqualification but an inevitability, the impact of which can be attenuated by exerting controls over factors causing it.

- Although rate and pattern of growth are fairly pre-defined in each case, they can be modified to some extent by improving living conditions.
- With the knowledge of broad generalizations about growth and its influencing factors geneticists can predict future growth and development of a child. Prediction equations have rather been worked out for almost all aspects of growth.

FORCES INFLUENCING GROWTH

Two major forces which influence an individual's growth and development are heredity and environment. While heredity is fixed and unchangeable factor, environment is flexible and modifiable. Every individual can be differentiated and identified on the basis of his genetic material which he inherits from his biological parents. This genetic material called DNA of which the genes are made is transmitted from generation to generation strictly according to natural laws, determines the basic traits of every individual both physiologenic and ontogenic.

Therefore, the hereditary characteristics are unmodifiable and unchangeable. There is substantial empirical evidence to prove that children born and brought up under most appropriate environmental conditions, reach the usual physical stature prevalent in the family. Height-weight patterns, complexion, susceptibility to certain physical ailments and psych-somatic disorders, motor and physiological capacity and many more characteristics are contained in the genetic material which the individual inherits.

No external influence can change or modify them. The individual variations in growth are largely due to these factors. It is said that if one wanted to be an Olympic athlete, one must choose one's parents carefully. Certain races are predisposed to grow taller and heavier than others.

Environmental factors include family atmosphere, parental care, medical facilities, neighbourhood, school, culture, society, climate, surroundings, shelter etc. The children from colder environments appear to grow healthier and stronger. It has been observed that the children belonging to poor, disturbed, and under-nourished families are significantly poorer in growth and health standards than children belonging to well-nourished and less disturbed families.

Similarly parental roles, peers, opportunity for education, society, culture influence growth. Environment factors and conditions affecting growth can be manipulated and modified but they cannot transgress heredity limits in terms of potential which is pre-determined. They simply add or substract to what one is endowed with. Researchers emphasises that innate capacity for growth "is a gift of nature. It can be guided, but is cannot be transcended by an educational agency."

MOTOR DEVELOPMENT

In order to have a better estimation of the role of physical activity in the development of a child, it is necessary to know a few vital facts about motor development through various periods of growth.

Infancy, as explained before, is a period of tremendous growth. In the beginning the general movements of the infant are uncoordinated. When a sensory stimulus is applied to one part of the body, the entire body is activated and the energy is diffused through out. The infant cannot make differentiated responses.

However, the general responses of the babe are visual-fixation on light, spontaneous eye movements, shuddering, shedding tears, sucking, swallowing, cheek and lip movements, sucking of the fingers, yawning, hiccuping, rhythmic mouthing movements, frowning and wrinkling of the brow, tuning and lifting the head, turning the trunk, body jerk, hand and arms movements, prancing and kicking legs etc. As the nervous system gains strength, during the first year of his life, the baby performs such motor activities as lifting his head while lying on his stomach, rolling from stomach to back, sitting, crawling, standing, assisted walking and finally unassisted walking. Essentially guided by cephalocaudal, proximo—distal and mass-to-specific principles, the motor development in infancy initiates adaptive and adoptive processes which bring the child face to face with realities of the world.

In childhood, rate of growth decelerates. As a consequence, the child starts learning new movements and has an urge for independent action. A child can jump off the floor at 37.3 months, stand on one foot alone at 29.3 months, hop at 49.3 months and throw into the basket at 61.5 months. He learns literally no new activity after fifth year but through repetition and practice, he over-learns various motor skills, with the result that there is gradual but sure improvement in the quality of performance.

By the time, the child enters puberty, he can perform variety of motor activities with equal dexterity, if he had been exposed to activity-environment early. Acquisition of high-coordination motor skills greatly depends on the interest, aptitude and opportunity in which children at this stage of life differ from one another significantly.

Adolescence is again a period of accelerated growth more in terms of bull and size rather than motor abilities. Due to increase in muscular strength, children can perform more vigorous activities and for longer duration. Motor development reaches its peak during adolescence. A close relationship is discernible between body-build and motor activities. The mesomorphic child who develops bulky muscles and thick bones likes to engage in games and sports requiring strength and speed. The ectomorph with thin and slender body frame goes in for endurance—type activities. The children with endomorphic heavy build get interested in activities. The children with endomorphic heavy build get interested in activities which require enormous strength like weightlifting, throwing, wrestling etc. Those who were deprived of opportunity for organized physical activity in early years show clumsy motor movements and are least inclined to sports. Such children have the tendency to become bookworms. Physical and motor strengths and weaknesses are clearly visible in the adolescents.

EXERCISE AND GROWTH RELATIONSHIP

Of all the factors which influence child's growth, physical activity is the most dynamic as well as important factor. The effects of physical activity on the organism are observable and measurable objectively. It is interesting to note that genetic factors generally resist digression from the normal growth pattern and strive to hold the original developmental scheme. Consequently, the effects of exercise tend to gradually disappear after the cessation of exercise.

Therefore, the continuity in growth and continuity in exercise are simply hand in glove. Recent research indicates that improvement in muscular development and efficiency is not due to growth of new muscle fibres but on account of activation of the inactive fibres and thickening of existing ones, chiefly due to vigorous physical exercise. It is obvious that muscle potential is greatly dependent on intensity rather than duration of exercise.

Although the morphological structure is predetermined yet it appears that endurance-type exercises stimulate more muscular vascularization because of the greater demands of circulation imposed by aerobic work on the cardiovascular system. On the other hand, more intense exercise seems to improve the muscle contents like proteins, myoglobin, muscle glycogen etc. and also the size of the muscle. However, it is not clear at present whether the muscular improvement, is due to mechanical involvement of tension and pressure or due to chemical phenomenon. Certain studies, especially of the German physiologists, show that exercise stimulates growth in the muscle only when oxygen debt occurs. Another view is that exercise causes changes in the muscle and when the muscle starts recovering, it overcompensates i.e., its recovery is more than what it has lost, resulting in improvement. Another important feature of the growth influences of exercise is that exercise causes reduction in the fat content of the body which is more in males than in females.

Exercise-physiologist also assert that the physical force affecting the orientation of muscle matrix of cell may alter the structural design of the muscles. Because of this reason the muscles developed in aerobic exercise are usually slender, thinner and longer and the muscles developed in anaeorobic exercises are stronger, shorter, and more spherical carrying more of explosive power.

The shape of muscles can be changed by switching over to either type of exercises. The most convincing explanation for this phenomenon is that exercise brings about certain definite positive changes in the central nervous system which plays a dominant role in growth and development.

It has also come to light that the weight of the internal organs, bone-strength and length are improved by exercise. It appears that the pressure-effects of exercise on the epiphytes of bones stimulates growth. But, if the exercise pressure is in excess, the growth of the bone retards Inactivity results in the slender, lighter and longer bones. The decline in structural growth is mainly due to loss of calcium and nitrogen as a result of inactivity or sedentary life-style.

As the shape of a muscle is modified by the quality of exercise; the shape of the bones also appears to be modified by variation in the quality of exercise. Heavy and resistance exercises develop stronger and thicker bones while light and long-duration exercises develop longer and thinner bones. As the angle of pressure application on the bones varies from exercise to exercise, the bony discs are rearranged according to the pressure application affecting the structure and shape of the bones.

Exercise and growth, therefore, are very closely related. All things being equal, the exercisers have more qualitative growth than non-exercisers.

PRIMACY OF MUSCULAR SYSTEM

Although all the systems of the body are interrelated and interdependent, the muscular system is considered as the prime instrument of movement. In the evolution of life, muscular system seems to have played an extremely important role.

In the living organisms, muscular system was the first to appear. The other systems developed only in relation to the activity of the muscular system. Differentiation in cells came about much later. This process was responsible for the creation of new animal species and made the higher animals like man extremely complex in structure and function. Protozoa and amoeba from which shot off other animal species in the beginnings are still a muscle. The visceral organs in higher animals developed in relation to the activity of the large muscles of the trunk.

The movement of a newborn child are largely big-muscle movements initially controlled by reflexes. The control over trunk muscles is more accurate and comes much earlier than control over extremities and fine muscles. The reason for this phenomenon is to be sought in the order and sequence of the foetal growth as well as evolutionary process. The trunk muscles, therefore, are the oldest. They play a pivotal role in the growth and development of the muscles of the extremities. 80% or the bulk of human body is all muscle. That is, perhaps the reason why muscular system should take precedence over other systems of the body.

More importantly, the cardiac, respiratory, mesentric and peristaltic muscles are not within the voluntary control of the individual. They are controlled primarily by reflexes. The skeletal muscles exert indirect control over these highly specialized muscles. The functional efficiency of the visceral muscles and organs is traced to efficient movement of the skeletal muscles.

The muscular system serves as an axis of man's life activity. On the basis of their structure and function, the muscles of the human body are categorized under the following heads:-

(i) Smooth muscles;

(ii) Cardiac muscles;

(iii) Striated muscles.

The smooth cells make smooth muscles which comprise the intestinal track. The cardiac cell make myocardium of which the heart is made. The digestive and cardiac musculature performs highly specialized functions of supplying food stuff and oxygen to all parts of the body for performing their respective functions.

The smooth muscles and cardiac muscles are not under the voluntary control of the individual but they are intimately related to the skeletal muscles. The visceral organs are not capable of improving their own efficiency, they depend on muscular system. The large muscles, when exercised vigorously, stimulate the visceral muscles to work at optimal efficiency.

From the skeletal musculature rather than the visceral muscles. By virtue of their structure, striated muscles are capable of producing powerful contractions. Each muscle fibre is composed of functional units referred to as sacromeres, which give the muscle fibre its striated appearance. Striations are caused by a repetitive and specific organization of the myofibriller proteins, actin and myocin and regulatory proteins within each sacromere. Skeletal muscles are attached to the bones: they have their origins and insertions. They exert their effect by moving parts to which they are attached or by compressing the parts they surround. When attached to the bones, the contracting muscle draws its two ends towards the centre and one or both attachments move. When the muscle is in the wall of the organ the contraction causes compression or movement, depending upon the position of the muscle cells.

MUSCLE TONE

The quality of the muscles to "remain in a state of semicontraction even when no activity is being performed", is called muscle tone or tunas. No powerful movement can occur unless the muscles are in a state of readiness. In simple words, the muscle tone is tension—a sort of tightness which keeps the muscle "set" for action. The muscle tone depends upon electrical stimulation from the nervous system and is a reflex phenomenon.

It is established beyond doubt that if the nerve that innervates a muscle is severed, the muscle becomes exceedingly flaccid. Endurance of the neuro-muscular system is closely related to the ability of a muscle to maintain tension when it is repetitively stimulated. All the living organisms even when completely relaxed, remain in a state of semi-preparedness, more popularly known as the semi-contraction phase.

During powerful contraction phases, there is rush of blood to the affected muscle and through chemical processes, heat is produced. The tonus is actually the cause of muscle development but if the tension so developed crosses the required level, it causes fatigue, makes the muscle stale, negatively affects movement-precision and impedes performance.

The only way to keep the muscles toned is to exercise them correctly and adequately. It is a fact that the muscles lose tone in old age. They also lose tone in bound age when one does not extract work out of them. Inactivity is the greatest enemy of the muscle tone. Frequent strains, sprains and pulls occur in the muscles because they are not properly toned through exercise.

Recent research had has revealed that the muscles get better toned through isogonic and isokinetic exercise rather than by long endurance-type activities. The well-toned muscles are of great advantage to man.

First, they help to maintain good posture in all situations. Not only do they give a beautiful look to the human body, they add to the work efficiency of the individual. The exercisers and non-exercisers have been found to differ significantly in this respect.

Second, a good muscle tone improves reaction tune, thereby enabling the sport-persons to perform better especially in short-duration speed events.

Third, improvement in neuro-muscular coordination is possible only when muscles are kept well-toned through exercise. This postpones early fatiguing and aging so that one can maintain good health and fitness even in old age.

RECIPROCAL INNERVATION

The muscles are arranged in pairs i.e. agonists and antagonists, in order to work in a cooperative and synchronized way. Biceps-triceps and quadriceps-hamstring are excellent examples of paired muscles. The agonists are called *prime movers* and antagonists controllers. When a group of agonists is stimulated and is initiating a movement, its opposite group acts as a counter force to regulate and control movement by relaxing.

This role of the paired muscles is reversed when the movement is performed in the exactly opposite direction.

While the movement of one group of muscles is guided by excitatory processes, the movement of its opponents is controlled by inhibitory processes. This natural phenomenon of checks and balances is called Reciprocal Innervation and is programmed through neural impulses.

Muscles are known to be servants of the brain and the volitional movements are initiated by impulses that are discharged from certain areas of the cerebral cortex. An important feature of this reflex activity is that stimulation of a particular muscle is associated with inhibition of the antagonistic muscle. The more intense the impulse, the more powerful the contraction in muscles and more violent the movement. A reticular formation in the brain is said to be the switchboard for excitatory and inhibitory processes in the muscles. Some muscles are called as fixators or stabilizers.

During a complex movement, when numerous group of muscles operate the anatomical levers, fixators hold these levers in their proper position. A wholesome activity programme must strengthen reciprocal innervation. The largely reflex-controlled movement of infants and children look clumsy in the beginning because their antagonists are not strong enough to control the movement and relax properly when agonists are contracting.

The principle of reciprocal innervation also underlines the fact that children should not be motivated beyond permissible limits and exercises involving too much of suppleness should not be given to very bound children because such exercises exert undue pressure on the spinal muscles and ligaments thereby severely affecting the inhibitory processes.

USE, DISUSE AND OVER USE

Free and unrestricted movement of muscles is a biological hunger. Life appears to go much better with vigorous motion than with inactivity. Biologists have conclusively proved that organs of the body which are in constant use, develop and remain efficient and those which are not used atrophy and become defunct.

The eternal law of use and disuse is said to be responsible for appearance of numerous characteristics in man and animals, and disappearance of others during the biological evolution. An astounding difference between an organism and a machine is that the former develops with use, the latter wears out. This does not rule out degeneration of the human body. The body does degenerate with age but the rate of wear and tear of cells can be minimized considerably and the repair work speeded up through well planned physical activity.

The exerciser does not turn old fast and continues to remain fighting fit even in declining years. 'Use' means proper and adequate movement of the body and its parts. 'Disuse' means cessation of activity or inadequate movement. So long a person is alive, there is no cessation of activity by simply attending to daily chores cannot be considered adequate if one is to enjoy the blessings of life.

The changed earthly—environment and the emergence of 'push-button culture' have considerably reduced the demands on the human body resulting in lower levels of health and organic fitness. The 'civilized' man is not required to jump a stream, climb a tree throw a stone in order to escape from danger or hunt for food. The challenges of modern civilization are entirely different from those encountered by man during evolutionary and revolutionary periods of life.

Yet challenges are challenges and they have to be met with verve and vigour if the human race has to survive as a virile master of creation rather its lazy-servant. The greatest danger to mankind is from physical inactivity and self-complacency about fitness and health. In a sense, modern life many be active but it certainly is not vigorous.

'Overuse' means working the muscles beyond their latent capacity. This generally happens when a commoner continues to work overtime to make both ends meet and an athlete trains hard and continuously without giving opportunity to the muscles to relax and recover from fatigue.

Stress fracture, muscle-soreness and staleness are some effects of overuse of muscles. Over using is overdoing, a consequence of over-motivation and over-enthusiasm. Physical exercise becomes a killer if the work-out is not properly planned. Training schedules planned without reference to nutrition, rest, load, intensity, capacity etc. not only retard performance, they pose a great threat to health and well-being of the athletes.

Physical education must teach people how to make judicious use of the muscles in order to receive benefits in terms of fitness for life and sport, health and wellness. Both disuse and overuse of muscles are dangerous in as much as one results in atrophy the other in hypertrophy. The middle path, therefore, is use—proper and adequate.

LOAD, CREST LOAD AND OVER LOAD

It has been scientifically established that real benefits from physical activity accrue only when its intensity and load are progressively increased. The principle of load has, therefore, great significance for physical educators. It is directly related to the cardio-respiratory system of the body. A load is considered as normal if the intake of oxygen is just adequate to meet the demands of the body.

During vigorous physical effort, when the entire cardio-respiratory machinery is working at a high rate, and the intake of oxygen is sufficient to continue work without problem, it is normal load. A load is considered to the be the crest load if the intake of oxygen is adequate to meet the demands of the body but the cardio-respiratory machinery is working at its optimum capacity without further prospectus of increase at that moment.

A load is considered over-load when the intake of oxygen is insufficient to meet its demand in the body even though the cardio-respiratory machinery works at its maximal capacity. This situation, when continued for sometime creates an imbalance in the demand and supply of oxygen and the oxygen debt results.

A few common signs and symptoms of over-loading physical activity are persistent soreness and stiffness in the muscles, tendons and joints, heaviness in legs, headache, nausea, loss of appetite, fatigue, sluggishness, loss of weight, swelling of the lemonades in the neck, groin and armpits, nervousness, depression, gasping for air, and unexplained drop in performance. During hard days of training , muscle fuel called glycogen is used up. It takes the body ten hours to ten days to replenish it. Potassium, a mineral released from the muscle cell to control heat is also depleted. It requires upto forty-eight hours to restore the supply.

Notwithstanding the serious athletic training where tow much overloading has to be the rule, the normal daily physical exercise is not adequate for optimum growth and development of a normal person. Although in the process of maturation various organs of the body develop yet more than normal work-load should be given on the body if greater efficiency and capacity are to be built up.

In the process of maturation, muscles and organs grow up in a normal way. For higher than the normal level of fitness and efficiency, sport scientists believe, muscles should be exercised at a higher than the normal work load. The optimal development of all parts of the body cannot be assured without application of this principle in letter and spirit. With repetition and practice i.e. through a psycho-physiological adaptation over a period of time, what is overload today, may become crestload tomorrow, and the crest load normal load day after. Progression is the keynote to the load-principle.

In training for competitive sports, overload is a rule rather than exception. Almost all serious sports require the athletes to be superfit. Unbelievable performance-records have been established in the Olympic games simply because the winning athletes had trained at a much higher load simply because the winning athletes had trained at a much higher load than required, thereby pushing up their physiological efficiency to the levels hitherto unknown, and extending frontiers of human body beyond the known horizons. For example, Paavo Nurmi—the hero of 1920 Olympics trained himself by running 50 fast miles a week while Emil Zetopack of 1956 Olympics, ran 70 fast miles per week so as be able to show unprecedented excellence in endurance running.

An important implication of the overload principle for the physical educators is that the physical activity load for various age groups and two sexes should be worked out in such a manner that physical activity assists growth and does not stunt it. Overloading of children when they are passing through accelerated periods of growth, is dangerous because it results in burning up.

A lot many promising athletes reach the deadened of their sporting career because over-enthusiastic teachers overload them with hard training and make them win junior competitions. Educationally this is not at all sound.

AGE : CRITERION OF PUPIL-CLASSIFICATION

From cradle to coffin, the human beings pass through various periods of growth and development. Each period of growth is unique in terms of its span and the characteristics of behaviour associated with it. From the viewpoint of universal norms of growth infants, children and adolescents differ from one another significantly in almost all characteristics. So classifying pupils into various groups on the basis of their chronological age poses no problem. The greatest difficulty comes from the individual differences amongst children of the same age group. Normally, chronological age is used as a yardstick for measuring growth of children and assigning to them social status. From the viewpoint of curriculum planning in physical education this socially recognized age-old practice has not been found very sound chiefly due to acute individual differences in growth and development. The geneticists, therefore, suggest that alongwith chronological age, developmental characteristics should also be taken into consideration when classifying pupils and assigning them to various groups.

A reference to anatomical, physiological and mental ages, which reflect various developmental characteristics, is a necessity. In common parlance, age virtually refers to chronological age which is reckoned in years, months and days.

Beginning with the day of birth and terminating with the death of an individual, the chronological age is guided by the moving hands of the clock. Traditionally, chronological age is a legally valid criterion for categorizing an individual into a minor or major person, seeking admission in a school, being eligible for a job, getting assigned to an athletic group—sub-junior, junior or senior—for sport competitions. Some physiologist reports that age is an important consideration upto almost seventeen years by which time a child is said to have grown upto 95%. After this, it should be discounted for classifying pupils solely on the basis of chronological age. Before a child reaches the top of maturity, chronological age as a criterion of classification might be misleading because various aspects of development do not necessarily move in a synchronized way. Some clever parents deliberately hide the actual age of their children with some ulterior motive. The sport associations do the same thing on purpose.

Anatomical age is concerned with ossification of bones—a process by which the elastic bones of the child become harder and stronger over a period of time with marked changes in their chemical composition. X-rays are generally used to determine the extent to which a child has matured structurally. Dentition—the number of teeth a child has at a particular point of time—is also considered as an index of anatomical age. This process of skeletal examination does not only lend credibility to the chronological age especially when the vested interests attempt to hoodwink the selectors for selecting subjunior and junior athletic teams but also help the physical educators to assess the suitability of children for strenuous physical activity and hard heavy weight training.

Determining anatomical age of a child is a highly technical task and should be left to the competent medical personnel. The physical educators should not resort to this technique without medical support. Physiological age is inferred from the signs and symptoms connected with puberty. It takes cognizance of the functional condition of the organs of the body more specifically the reproductive and the glandular systems.

The quality and quantity of hair on the pubis and in arm pits, onset of menarche in girls and night ejaculation in boys are sure indices of age-related developmental changes and physiological maturity of children. Even though a valid yardstick of pupil classification, physiological age is rarely calculated unless clinical situations so warrant. Besides, determining physiological age of a child is a cumbersome task. The teachers/parents have to venture into the private life of the children to assure themselves of maturity level. Despite all this, physiological readiness/maturity is an important consideration in working our activity load for each child especially when he/she is inducted into the arena of competitive sport at a relatively young age.

Mental age indicates maturity of the human mind especially cognitive, perceptual and affective abilities. Developmental psychologists consider mental age as an important classification—criterion. In skill-acquisition, mental maturity is of great value. Mentally backward children find it difficult to acquire sports skills speedily. Even though mental age is rarely used as a yard stick for pupil classification in sport activity circles, numerous performance and paper-and-pencil tests are available which can help the physical educators to differentiate deviant mental growth curve from the normal one. Physical educators should be well advised not to lean too heavily on chronological age even though it serves as a handy tool for pupil classification.

Other variables such as high as height, weight strength, aerobic/anaerobic capacity, mental maturity etc. require serious consideration while classifying pupils and assigning them to various groups.

HEALTH AND EXERCISE

Generally, health means 'freedom from disease'. When discussed in relation to human movement, health seems to be a much broader concept and this definition is found lopsided. Health, is "that quality of life which enables one to live are two different things. There are many who have rarely fallen prey to any serious disease in life but this does not at all mean that they really 'live most and serve best.' Health, therefore, has mental, social and spiritual implications.

The crux of the matter is that 'freedom from disease' is only one aspect of health. One needs to have a fairly high level of physical fitness to perform one's duties to the best of one's ability, to be free from mental tensions, to have a healthy attitude towards life, and to have an excellent rapport with one's environment. Only then one would certainly enjoy the blessings of nature and live optimally. A healthy person should not live for himself, he must significantly contribute to create a healthy environment—both physical and social—in order to make the world a better place to live in. This exactly is the underlying spirit of the phrase 'live most and serve best'. It is wisely said that a healthy person is an asset to the society, a sick person a liability. The one commands and the other simply demands.

SEX AND AGE DIFFERENCES

Biologically, the sex of a child is determined at the very moment of conception and a neonate enters this world wither as a male or female. Nature has ordained the sexes to play their respective roles according to biological requirements especially in the matter of procreation. Structural and functional differences between the genders are innate. They have a great bearing on the social roles the sexes play in their life.

From the view-point of growth and development, except for distinction in reproductive system, the differences in physical structure and function of female and male child are hardly manifest until puberty. With the onset of puberty which is about two years earlier for the female child, the secondary sex characteristics begin to appear and become quite pronounced during "teens" in the two sexes. From here onward does the parting-of-ways commence for the male and the female.

The differences characterizing sexes are not merely superficial but significant because even a layman considers them so profound that it is regarded as an insult to refer to a person to the other sex than that to which he or she rightly belongs. "It is here", say Lindhard "that the object of their education must differ in the same degree because the boys must be brought up to be men and girls to be women."

The structural, physiological and emotional differences that surface during adolescence are essentially due to the functioning of sex glands and the effects that follow transform delicate girls into beauteous women and boys into virile young men, both capable of reproductive activity. The gonads not only produce the germ-plasm—the material cause of a new life—but also secrete hormones which give respective secondary characteristics to the sexes.

Characteristically, girls have a faster growth rate in the early stages of adolescence. They are ahead of boys atleast by two years. The growth-spurt begins by 10-11 years in girls and 11-13 in boys. Even by 14-16 years, boys are behind girls in maturity. After that the boys not only grow faster but also they overtake girls. By 16-17 years, girls reach the peak of their growth when the boys are still midway. The greatest impact of growth-spurt, both in boys and girls, is found in the anatomical and physiological regions.

When the growth-curves of the two sexes are compared, it would not be difficult to find that (1) the girls mature earlier than boys, and (2) they temporarily surpass the boys in physical dimensions around mid-adolescence. The faster growth-rate and shorter growth-span make the girls look maturer than boys. By 16-17 years the female growth-rate slackens down considerably, while the male growth-curve continues to show an upward trend well upto 19-20 years.

On this account, women are said to be "aging" faster and their life-span, on average, is found to be shorter in comparison to that of man.

ANATOMICAL DIFFERENCES

- The skeletal height, which is genetically determined, is the most important index of growth. By nature, man is taller and heavier than woman. Even at birth, an average male infant is longer by an inch or so than the female child.
- The female bones are comparatively shorter and weaker. As a result, the entire female skeleton is shorter, less angular and more delicate. Since much of the female muscle is all-fat, the skeleton shows

marked muscle traces. This makes women susceptible to negative effects of hard manual labour.

- The proportion between torso and extremities in both the sexes is different. While women have a comparatively longer torso and shorter limbs, men have shorter torso and longer limbs. This structural arrangement may not be an oddity but this creates many a mechanical complication for women in activities which necessitate 'body reach' and frequent change of centre of gravity. Shorter limbs and longer body makes the female centre of gravity. Shorter limbs and longer body makes the female centre of gravity fall lower. That is why, women have a greater stability in body balance better than men.

- The lumber region of the female spine is comparatively longer and the thoracic region shorter. The narrow thoracic cavity makes no room for bigger visceral organs as in man. Woman's heart, lungs, stomach etc. are smaller than those of man.

- The greater difference is in the pelvic region. The female pelvis is much roomy and broader. It is so because women have to rear children inside their body. The uterus on this account is distensible so that even the pelvic bone itself is broader. Thus, the abdominal wall which is the main support of viscera, is a wailer part in women especially those who have given birth to children. The greater and stronger use of lower extremities requires a fairly strong and solid pelvic girdle which is not there in women. In this respect, women are not stronger or even equal to men.

- Woman's shoulder is much weaker than that of man. Not only the bones of the shoulder joint but also the muscles and cartilages controlling the movement of the shoulder joint, are weaker. The clavicles are comparatively long and slender. Consequently women are far inferior to man in shoulder strength. That is, perhaps, the reason why hanging exercises in gymnastics and pole vault are not prescribed for women. In swinging bat or racquet and throwing a ball women are far behind man.

- Because of the pelvic bone being broader and longer, the comparatively greater convergence of the thigh bones result in knees being slightly inward, and that on crux, when the position of the femur is more vertical as in running, points obliquely downward-outward. Due to this skeletal arrangement, the female lower extremities lose both force and precision. Broader hips, unlike those of men, are a hindrance in running and also in movements requiring more of agility. The sway of hips in walking impinges upon the energy cost.
- Slender bones and rounded fatty muscles make women inferior to men in almost all the regions of strength, i.e., grip strength, explosive strength, dynamic strength etc. Their punch, thrust, kick, hit pull, push etc. much lighter than those of men.

PHYSIOLOGICAL DIFFERENCES

- On the whole, muscular strength in women is far less than in men. Due to slightly different composition of muscles and abundance of adipose tissue, no amount of weight training can help women improving muscular strength and power. Man is much stronger to woman in pulling, pushing punching, slapping, kicking, striking, and squeezing.
- Not only are women misfit for hard manual labour but even at light physical duties, they do not have the same staying power as men. Their aerobic capacity is very low and during vigorous activity their muscle glycogen gets depleted at a much faster rate as compared to men. Asmussan, a Danish

physiologist, has set the strength of the average female at 60% of the male figure, with only about a half of this deficiency being attributed to her shorter stature.

- Comparatively smaller cardio—respiratory apparatus of women is greatly responsible for their low vital capacity and stroke volume. Their heart rate is faster. Variations in their blood composition favour certain biological functions which women perform. All this affects their endurance capacity.

- Menstrual-period, which bogs down a woman atleast for five days in a month, has been a debatable point with exercise physiologists as well as female athletes for a long time. Not withstanding sociological merits and demerits of the case, the medicos are in agreement that except in extreme pathological cases, the 'periods' do not affect women's physical strength. The menstrual period has greater psychological implications than physiological complications. Headache, nausea, sluggishness, inaptitude for vigorous activity etc. are observed in menstruating women.

- Interestingly, in normal circumstances, atleast one woman in seven is liable to be menstruating on any day. Sport physiologists have, therefore, been able to alter the menstrual periods of female competitors so that this inevitable biological activity does not create hurdles during international fixtures. Surprisingly, some women athletes are said to have successfully spell. Still the medical world does not react favourably to women's tendency of subjecting themselves to hard physical training and competition during the menstrual period on hygienic and health grounds.

- Pregnancy and child-bearing are very sensitive situations in the life of a woman during which she cannot be subjected to hard physical activity. These biological functions make women different to men and restrict their freedom of movement. During pregnancy and especially after childbirth light exercise is essentially necessary for women but not without consultation of a doctor. No wonder, some mothers compete in international sports competitions. These are exceptions. The average woman cannot dream of it. General health condition—both internal and external is the major consideration in this matter.

- Even though average man's brain weights 3 pounds, the average woman's two pounds, the relation of the brain to body is about the same in both sexes and, in any case, it does not make woman inferior to man in intelligence. However, women are found to be inferior to man in reaction time and less predisposed to aggressiveness. Women are slower in motor reactions such as in applying brakes to speeding automobiles.

- Women have also been found emotionally weak. The effect of injury, accident, victory or defeat is far greater on women than on men. Women may not be lacking in self-control but once they breakdown under stress, they take more time to recover from shocks and traumas. Manifestation and effects of nervous breakdown are far stronger in women than in men. That is perhaps, why experts do not advise women exposing themselves to activities which disturb emotional equipoise such as boxing where a hard punch from the opponent may set the athlete bleeding.

- Sex and age differences are not at all a quash for anxiety because spheres of sports competition and physical activity for men and women are clearly demarcated. Age groups and sexes do not clash with one another on the sports field but compete in their own categories. The knowledge of sex and age differences serves as an excellent guidelines for planning exercise and sport curricula for various slices of population and organizing competition for them.

5

THE IMPORTANCE OF PHYSICAL TRAINING IN PHYSICAL EDUCATION

Physical training means planned physical exercises performed systematically in schools and youth organization for educational purposes. Its aims are manifold. The emphasis is generally laid on its preventive medical aspect: physical training should promote health and develop-physical strength and endurance. It also has subsidiary aims the importance of which varies from one country to another, such as pre-military training, social training, character and will formation and training in posture and efficiency.

Physical training as an educational subject did not become worldwide until the last two centuries with the advent of compulsory education. Very few schools or youth organization do not nowadays include it in their syllabus. In different countries it takes a variety of form corresponding to its subsidiary aims.

It is highly complex, but the one factor common to all it forms is movement. Physical movements effort and performance are always its foundations and its essential characteristics. The idea that physical movement is an important factor in education has now spread to all parts of the world.

The diversity of physical training and its lack of uniformity throughout the world are due to its historical development. Modern physical training is a river fed from many sources. Its oldest source and its most beautiful manifestation in the European countries are the gymnastics of ancient Greece.

Besides those it comprises many popular forms of games, contests and dance coming from all over the world: gymnastics from the monasteries of China; Indian breathing and concentration exercises; ball games from the Indians and from the Middle ages in Europe; the tournaments of chivalry; the swimming sports of the South Sea Islanders; skiing from the Lapps and Scandinavians; canoeing from the Eskimos.

Those early forms of local culture have converged from all sides to stimulate physical training and to be adopted by it and transformed.

In this nineteenth century it received powerful impetus from the German gymnastic movement, from Swedish gymnastics and from the sports and games of English life. The English development in particular spread its influence throughout the world. The sports and games of the British nobility passed in unbroken succession to the middle classes and during the nineteenth century to the workers, preserving the ethical, social and spiritual values of chivalry but adapting them to the needs of the times. Sociologists agree that modern sport as it developed in Great Britain between 1880 and 1900 was a by-product of the industrial revolution.

Every country that has developed industries and become an industrial nation can show a parallel development of sport. The latest evidence for this observation comes from the Soviet Union and Bharat. We can see today that the form of English sport, with its contests and games and its spirit of "fairness", has spread to nearly every country in the world probably as one manifestation of a uniform and universal culture. This modern sport has also decisively influenced physical training, in many lands very much, in others for the time being not at all.

Throughout the world, however, discussion takes place on the influence of sport on physical training, and a modern physical training without sport is today inconceivable.

In the twentieth century, moreover, physical training has received a new access of strength from modern gymnastics and modern dancing, which first appeared in Central Europe and were then developed on a large scale in the schools of Great Britain.

When, as a consequence of compulsory education physical training appeared in all countries in the nineteenth century, its national components were preponderant. In Prussian Germany for instance German "school gymnastics" with their strictly formal and intellectual structure made headway against the great political difficulties of the anti-democratic restoration; in Sweden there grew up a system of health and pustular gymnastics that was adopted in many other countries; the public schools of England developed a training based on games which helped to shape the English national character. There appeared for the first time in the twentieth century a tendency for national systems of physical training to influence one another, which now seems to have reached some kind of settlement.

The German youth movement generated fresh impulses which brought physical training and gymnastics out of their dusty buildings back into nature. In Austria there grew up the "natural gymnastics" which overcame the rigid forms of gymnastics instruction and gave new life to physical training.

In France He'bert introduced his "method naturelle", which had a similar effect, Sweden likewise started to reform its unduly rigid methods. All these new movements spread their influence beyond the national frontiers. The Austrian innovations strongly influenced physical training in Holland and also in Germany. The reforms in Sweden and Germany were reflected in countries which had originally learnt physical training from them.

Two world wars brought upheaval and devastation but also strengthened the bonds between peoples. Physical training now manifests a general tendency to become uniform in all countries, and similar results of change can be observed in many places. The problems of physical training which confront us today are much the same over most of the world.

This statement sounds surprising, but at the first UNESCO seminar on physical training and sports held in Gauting Munich, in September 1957 it was generally agreed to be true.

What points are covered by agreement?

1. It is apparent in all countries that their large cities and industrial areas have so little room in which children can play and move that special measures have to be taken to promote children's active physical life. The most important measure of this kind is compulsory physical training in the schools.

2. It is also apparent everywhere that, to prevent our children from becoming intellectualized, these school which go in for nothing but book-learning must yield to the cultivation of physical, artistic and manual skills.

3. It is admitted in all industrial States that in free communities sports and games make an important contribution to social and moral training, which is now inadequate in communities using only traditional methods.

4. All State and municipal educational authorities therefore now agree in demanding a stronger, deeper and more vital physical training in schools and youth organizations.

That is the scope of agreement concerning the postulates of physical training. It is, however, interesting to note that the problems which physical training authorities have to tackle nowadays are much the same in all countries. They relate to methods, the training of instructors, and the finding of money for playgrounds and premises. The differences life merely in the matter which shall be taught, where historical and national factors are as important as ever.

I. Methods

It is a surprising thing that in the last ten years the old conflict over the best method of physical training has come to an end. Discussion always brings to the fore the "natural method"; it has various names and concepts according to language and national characteristics, but emphasis is always laid on freedom, the differences between individuals, pleasure, and indirect effects. It is widely known in Europe as the "movement lesson" though it has by no means been introduced into all schools. It allows the child independence, freedom of will, freedom of choice and freedom of fantasy development, but demands of him discipline and inward order. It is a democratic form of physical training and is therefore banned in the dictator States.

To develop it further is a universal task in which all nations participate in peaceful emulation and which is certain to bear precious fruit.

II. THE TRAINING OF INSTRUCTORS

The proper training of instructor for physical education is also a matter discussed in all countries. A final solution has not yet been reached any where, should physical-training instructors be trained in universities and teacher-training colleges, or in special high schools? Should the instructor be a specialist, or should he teach other subjects as well and be trained in these also? Should primary schools have physical-training instructors, or should the form masters give all the instruction, including that of physical training? What happens to physical training if, as in many countries, most of the teaching is done by women? These are the worldwide problems in this field. In Europe it is becoming increasingly probable that they will be solved along the following lines.

(i) In the higher schools the system of specialization in teaching prevails; the physical training instructor teacher other subjects as well, especially when he grows older.

(ii) The primary-school teacher must be thoroughly instructed in physical training so that he can teach it later in his own class.

(iii) Women who have been suitably trained are perfectly capable of conducting physical training in schools for boys only.

The standing of physical training in relation to other school subjects depends less on the teacher's practical ability than on his skill as a teacher and his moral attitude and character. Modern schools of all sorts need physical training instructors who know their subject inside out and are keen on it, and who at the same time are, as teachers and instructors, intellectually and scientifically equal and superior to their pupils.

III. PREMISES

The most difficult problem of physical training in all countries is that of premises and equipment. War damage has made it just as accrue in many European countries as it is in countries such as Turkey and Egypt where physical-training organization is new. The construction of playgrounds, halls, swimming baths and playing field needs a big capital outlay and their maintenance means a continuing expense. For instance in Germany, with its unfavourable climate, an ideal programme for the building of gymnasia would cost DM3,000 million, or 7.5 percent of the national budget. How can parliaments and parties be convinced that such expenses are vital for the future of our people?

In Great Britain the Education Act, 1944, has shown that they can be so convinced. The most powerful help in this fight for money for physical training comes from the doctors, who throughout the world are ardent champions of physical training as a weapon against the menacing disease of civilization. It is also important to develop a sound, convincing scientific theory of physical training, without which such a vital movement can nowadays make no headway.

It is absolutely necessary to press forward with the development of the practical side of teaching but theory in research and instruction must no be neglected. An international physical-training research institution, perhaps within the scope of UNESCO, would be for many countries an inestimable aid and support in the campaign for sound physical training.

IV. THE SCOPE OF INSTRUCTION

The difference between countries in the choice of the subjects to be taught in physical training is relatively wide. Historical development, with its national and popular origins and forms, is here especially conspicuous. That however, is certainly no disadvantage.

On the contrary, modern methods of physical training do not depend on any hard-and-fast code of exercises and performance but can be applied to all forms of movement. The more varied the material offered, the better is the chance of making all children enthusiasts for movement. Physical training throughout the world has hitherto been shaped too preponderantly by Europe; we are now expecting it to receive a strong access of new life from the hitherto little-known ancient and popular forms of movement practised in , for instance, India, Japan and western Asia.

If we allow free competition, physical training will be enriched precisely by the interaction of national physical exercises with modern sports, and its results. We Europeans look with amusement and reverence on the methods and result of Yoga, and on the old Indian dances which have been so beautifully revived. The inner movement of meditation, and the artistic shaping of movements, are forms which ought to be brought within the reach of physical training.

It would be lamentable-and this is the last thing I have to say- if modern sport with its Anglo-Saxon stamp, though indispensable for physical training were to become the only prevailing form, the sole principle of physical training for the whole world. The Olympic games, based on the principles of sport, definitely guide the physical training of every country in this direction. There is most oftenly three principles operating in physical training: there is the principle of sport, the essence of which is the competitive comparison of measurable performance, and alongside it is the principle of true play, so well as the principle of gymnastic dancing, in essence the artistic moulding of movement. Until all three principles can stand side by side, equal in rights and rank and interpenetrate one another, we shall no have a physical training that is really effective and educationally, psychologically and biologically sound.

In addition, the physical training of every land should cultivate the traditional forms of the nation and people : in Germany gymnastics and walking, in Austria mountain climbing and skiing in England rowing and sailing, in Japan archery and club-fighting, in India perhaps Mallkhamb.

The great games of basketball, volleyball and football, track athletics and swimming have already made such headway in the world that there is now no danger that in any country, at least of the free world, physical training will recede into national restriction and one-sidedness.

The best way to encourage physical training in all countries is, however, for all those who have authority and knowledge in this domain to work together and pool their experience and knowledge in mutual help and support and in sporting comradeship and brotherhood.

6

THE IMPORTANCE OF GUIDANCE AND EDUCATION IN PHYSICAL EDUCATION

Perhaps the most marked features of a developed and industrialised culture are its fluidity and its complexity. Many of the highly developed cultures of the past were complex but, because of caste of class systems, they were relatively static; and the place in them of the individual participant was determined by the accident of birth. From then on, his education, his vocation, his marriage even, and much, if not all, of his moral and emotional life were determined for him by a series of rules and by a continuous social conditioning that allowed little possibility of emerging from "the station to which God had called him". Upward social mobility was restricted frequently to the most able or confined to periods of social disintegration under the impact usually of war, famine or pestilence, or it was permitted in one or two directions only-for example the artist craftsman of the Renaissance in Italy. It was always possible to fall from high estate, but such falls rarely meant a change of class. It is indeed possible to argue that the decline of many ancient cultures was marked by an incipient fluidity and upward mobility which undermined the social structure without allowing it to transform itself sufficiently. The Renaissance in Europe, on the contrary, by generalizing in Western culture the concepts of individualism of the uniqueness of the individual and by digesting in social terms the judo-Christian concept of the value of a human being in and for himself, may have provided the only possible psych-social situation in which social mobility, cultural complexity, and humanism are compatible with maintenance of steady evolution in society and the enrichment of personal life.

By values consciously and unconsciously determined and accepted, every culture makes a series of choices which, by facilitation of exclusion, guide individuals in their growth; and education is one of the major means of inculcating the "rightness" of these choices and of ensuring that the individual accepts them. We tend, however, naturally in our education of children-whether as parents or as teachers-to transmit the values of our culture and its choices in terms of our own childhood and adolescent experience.

On the other hand one of the features of contemporary life, whether in Western communities or in the so-called developing countries, is the rapidity of social change, the telescoping into a generation or even half a generation, of the growth and enlargement of material and personal possibilities which have been spread over centuries. It is important here to emphasize a fact that is frequently forgotten, namely that this is not merely a raising of the material standard of life, not merely a matter of better nutrition, protection from disease the accumulation of objects and instruments of use and beauty; it is an enlargement of the possibilities of riches in the emotional, intellectual and spiritual life. The bewilderment of choice, the hunger for possession, the apparent materialism are the superficial aspects of a process which should permit a flowering of the human spirit hitherto confined to a privileged few in exactly the same way as the motor car provides a chance of enlargement of experience which was frequently denied even to princes in their horse-drawn carriages

It is often stated that "you can't change human nature." In fact of course human nature does change and contemporary man is considerably different psychologically as well as socially from his medieval counterpart, or even from the nineteenth century man. The twentieth century may well prove ultimately to be more remarkable for the development of the human sciences, especially that of psychology, than for advances in the application of the physical sciences. One thing is certainly becoming clear from our growing knowledge of the way in which personality develop : that, while perhaps there may be biologically determined limitations upon personal growth and tendencies towards particular mental structures and rigidities, human nature is infinitely more modifiable than has hitherto been recognized or than at present we know how to exploit. Indeed it may well be hat the nature versus nurture controversies will seem academic not many years from hence as will some if not all of our conceptions of conditioning , learning and the like.

If the line of thought outlined above is correct, then the contemporary problem is that of exploiting the richness of possibilities offered by a fluid, complex culture of great mobility and in process of rapid change, by exploiting and developing the personal resources of contemporary man. In other words, whereas in the past we could accept relatively few variations in personality structure and a relatively short period of growth, conditioning, and adaptation, we can now envisage the possibility, even the desirability, of a widening range of differences in personal development and a longer period of growth leading to a more flexible, richer and more fully exploited use of the potential resources of each individual. Just as contemporary man is heavier and taller than his medieval counterpart, we may look to see an increase in creativity, imagination, subtlety and delicacy of intellectual and emotional response if the resources inherent in human psychology can be effectively exploited.

It is into this line of thought that our concepts of guidance should be fitted; and the idea is not a new one that education should aim to achieve the fullest possible realization of the possibilities inherent in the individual. The difficulty lies partly in our ignorance of human potentialities; partly in the resistances which develop in growing adult; and partly in our incapacity to exploit the techniques of education as a means of guiding and fostering the growth of the individual and through him of his society. The tendency of guidance in the past fifty years has been to concentrate upon the rehabilitation of the abnormal-the delinquent, maladjusted, or pathological individual-or it has sought an adaptation to circumstances, usually of work, which it does not seek to charge or even to modify. Thus one finds much discussion of vocational guidance as essentially a means of helping the individual to fit into the world of work and of selection or allocation to various forms of secondary studies considered mainly as a more or less efficient process of enabling the schools to receive the kind of pupils which they can educate in a predetermined way. "Child Guidance" too has become almost synonymous with the treatment of problem children. As is perhaps natural in such circumstances, the various kinds of services of guidance and those who staff them have tended more and more to become specialized and to be separated from the schools and from responsibility for the growth of society itself. Instead of becoming increasingly aware of the needs and directions of their social group and attempting to harmonize the potentialities of the young with the circumstances of a changing life, they are specialists concerned with a narrow sector in time.

However, in rare cases very clearly indeed, the educator sees that such guidance is not enough. The pioneers of active methods were certainly concerned with the immediate ease with which children could be brought to learn what adults thought it fit they should learn; but they were also concerned with fostering the kind of creativity peculiar to each child, and which, if exploited, night lead him to make an individual contribution to the growth of his community.

In this sense, guidance cannot be separated from the total educational process, even though some of its more complex functions may be discharged by specialists. Nor can it be a snapshot process. It must take account of what has made each child what he is and of what society wishes him to become—that is, at once of the social and environmental pressures that shape us, of the ways and means of modifying them, and finally of the ends, values, exigencies and choices of society. It derives from an implicit value system; it should be concerned with the analysis of this system and if necessary, participate in changing it progressively.

This is a point the implication of which may perhaps be illustrated by a negative example. We can now within fairly narrow limits select from among all children at the threshold of puberty, those most likely to profit from an academic type of secondary education. What in fact we do is to accept criteria of success as determined by the school or by examining bodies and proceed to develop tests or other procedures which give the best possible prediction. As this "guidance", become more efficient, the schools receive more and more children who are suitable to their methods and curricula. The danger is twofold : implicitly the values represented by the criteria come to be accepted as sacrosanct; and there are fewer and fewer of those partial misfits who constitute the challenge to educational method and the motive for improvement and rethinking. This is not to say that efficient selection or guidance is undesirable: far from it. It is to suggest that any should scheme of guidance-whether in the educational field or in the vocational field-must consider in value-term as well as in psychological ones, not only the child, his abilities and aptitudes but the situation of education or work, to which we wish him to adapt. It is not a simple affair of static matching, so many abilities or qualities in the subject, so many demands made by the situation. Both in the subject and in the situation there is or should be a process of modification, education in one sense, which finally fits them together leaving neither as it was before. We must also ask whether the criteria of successful adaptation ensure the real values which our society is seeking; or whether in efficiently adapting children to a situation which is intrinsically imperfect or even outmoded, we are not contributing rather to the stagnation or deterioration of society than it its dynamic improvement. Put in another way, we may say that long with the guidance of the individual should go a constant attempt to bring about evolution in the situation towards which we orient him.

But the development or stagnation of a society does not depend solely on what happens in its schools: nor can we be content at some stage in life merely to task children as the chances of their growth and experience have made them. At the time of beginning school, at eleven or twelve, when the child is on the threshold of adolescence with all its possibilities, at the end of compulsory schooling, and at many an other stage in his growth, we become aware that he is an individual with a history, and that many of the foundations of his personality and many of his attitudes and capacities depend upon events in his early childhood and upon what has gone on in his family, and in the streets, in his life outside the classroom.

We are not yet fully aware of how different kinds of experience may favourably or unfavourably modify growth; nor of what implications certain kinds of environmental pressure or facilitation may have for subsequent education and adjustment. We do, however, know many things : we know, for example, that if a child be deprived of certain experiences under the age of live, it is difficult if not impossible for him to grow satisfactorily later. If he lives in an environment where he gets little verbal stimulus we know that he will have difficulty ın the early stages of learning to read. We know too that if he is prevented by circumstances from play in as he should with all kinds of objects and substances, he will suffer severely later on and may well lose not only the capacity to play but any creative or constructive tendency whatever. In the past for most children, more or less by accident, the circumstances, of life in the country or in a small community provided them with what was necessary for relatively satisfactory psychological growth. In the huge urban concentrations of the present day, children do not get such things as space and materials for play, chances to explore their environment and the like, accidentally. They are lacking or severely curtailed, and they have to be provided. Just as manufactured food may be deficient in vitamins and just as these have to be supplied artificially ; so childhood's experiences may be deprived of the vitamins of effective and intellectual growth and we should recognize this and take steps to replace them.

Thus our concept of guidance as an intrinsic aspect of education must also include an analyst's of the environment in terms of the needs of children, the attempt to determine how these needs may be supplied by the family, by the school or by some other means, and the necessary help to parents and teachers which will enable them to discharge their functions. Again, however, the fundamental principle is illustrated that we cannot confine ourselves to bringing about an adaptation to the status quo on the one hand or to the treatment of exceptional case on the other. The circumstances in which many children grow up, the pressures, economic, social and psychological, upon them through their families and through the surrounding community are not ideal, may well be unacceptable.

There is thus the inescapable social responsibility of asking ourselves how the family may be adapted to contemporary life and how its surrounding circumstances may be ameliorated so that the values upon which we are agreed may be preserved and developed and at the same time the experiences of childhood may pave the way for the full flowering of creative human beings later on. This is not likely to be achieved by a kind of laissez-faire paternalism nor by focusing our effort on the so-called problem families, urgent as such first aid may be. It can only be done if our knowledge of sociology, of social psychology and of child development is put at the disposal of parents themselves, not in the form of easy instructions on child-rearing, but as an active instrument which enables them to achieve ends which they have consciously chosen for themselves and their children.

The need for this kind of guidance is perhaps most clearly seen in the technical assistance field. Here communities-or at least their leaders-have chosen certain objectives of economic and social development. As means to these ends they have attempted to develop certain kinds of educational system. In many cases, however, these systems do not achieve the ends sought because the implications of technology in psychological terms, or the content of curricula and of educational method do not square with the kinds of personality structure which the culture hitherto has favoured. Technological development, the spirit, of free scientific enquiry as it is understood by the West, an economy, based upon activity, competitiveness and aggression, may all require certain attitudes in the individual, themselves based upon the intangible pressures of childhood, which are absent in a particular culture. This does not mean that the ends of social or economic development should not be sought; it does mean that the way to achieve them may not be that of simply importing superficial aspects of systems which have apparently been successful elsewhere. One must search for and recognize the essentials; and these essentials are almost always psychological, tissues of disposition and attitudes in individuals and groups, reaching back deep into the culture and stemming from the unstructured experiences on early childhood, play with comrades, the pressures and predilections frequently unconscious, of the community within which each adult has grown. It may well be that the essential means of introducing any particular social or economic change is that of influencing the basic psychological climate in which the young grow up and which the adult takes for granted.

Just as a child cannot learn arithmetic unless he has first gone through the casual preschool experiences of counting, enumerating, weighing and measuring, upon which depend his basic concepts of number, size, weight, area and the like, so it may be that a community cannot have the aeroplane, the motor car, the refrigerator, sanitation, and a relatively healthy environment unless a considerable proportion of those who compose it have gone through some at least of the psychological experiences which led mankind to invent them. The problem is to determine the nature of these basic experiences, whether for the individual or for the culture, and then to ensure that they are provided.

The upshot of this rather discursive and undetailed discussion is to underline the idea that guidance is implicit in education-whether we are considering the guidance of parents, of school children, or of adolescents at the threshold of their career. But it should also be explicit. That is to say that it should increasingly become a continuous process of analysis and re-synthesis, a means whereby the insights of psychology, whether of the individual, his group, or of his society, are consciously used as a means to the enrichment of human life. Just as better nutrition and the removal of physical inhibiting factors have contributed to greater life span, to heavier, taller, and healthier human beings, so we should be able to attempt the subtler and more difficult task of releasing the human spirit from the psychological inhibitions which dampen or destroy the capacity for creativity and joy.

Much of this is a workaday task, requiring good journeyman common sense; and much of it is being done already. In Europe and North America, for example, the need for easing the transition from home to school has been recognized. Tests of school readiness of reading readiness, reception classes, nursery schools and classes all exist and are becoming more and more widely used. Many schools, in America, Austria, Canada, Britain, France and elsewhere, make use of cumulative record cards which serve as a means of recording the observations of different teachers upon the growth of their pupils and which may be the basis of curricular or methodological modifications. In some countries, guidance, on the basis mainly of objective tests, is given at the threshold of secondary education in order to aid children in the code of alternatives according to their aptitudes; and in most, there are service of vocational guidance, some highly developed like those of Belgium and Holland. Almost every country in Europe, North America, and a good many others in the rest of the world, alarmed at the increasing numbers of children who show marked signs of maladjustment or who become delinquent, has set up services of diagnosis and treatment, child guidance clinics and the like.

From such activities much good has resulted; and the study of the process of adjustment is bound to draw attention to many factor in human psychology which imply a criticism either of educational value or of the pressure exerted by society itself. Yet, as has been suggested earlier, we have yet to take two essential steps. The first is the integration of all services of guidance-whether for the preschool child and his parents, for the school child, or for the adolescent on the threshold of work-into a comprehensive and coordinated process conceived as the essential ancillary to the effort of the teacher. This step would recognize at once the integrity of the individual and the wide range of differences between individuals-a range which, since it is the source of riches in the life of a community-the service may be said to exist to foster.

The second step is perhaps more essential; it is certainly more difficult. Communities change, for good or for ill; they offer more or fewer possibilities to individual participants. We in Europe and probably in the world generally, are committed to rapid change and to the humanistic concept that all human being are of equal value though of different capacities. This implies that guidance services must also be concerned with the situations towards which the individual is guided. They must therefore, not become merely efficient means of selection; but instruments whereby the situation in which the child or adolescent finds himself-the family, the school, the working environment—is analysed in terms of how far it favours the full development of which he is capable and fosters a dynamic social contribution rather than deadens-as at present-his power to live fully.

7

THE ROLE OF GUIDANCE AND COUNSELLING IN PHYSICAL EDUCATION

There have been countless voices, down through the ages, which have posed this problem-have presented this perennial dilemma. Ever since human beings have lived together in groups there have been conflict of interests and confusion of authorities. Only by the help the receives from other can the decisions of life be made : such help is *Guidance*. Those who are wiser and who have travelled the road before show the way to others.

Often, however, the word 'guidance' is used in a more restricted sense, to indicate a set of professional techniques. These includes methods such as the maintenance of records; the construction and application of tests; the use of various types of interviews-depth, non-directive, psychoanalytical; the use of questionnaires; role-playing, psycho-drama, even hypnosis, the use of rating system; the full bag of tricks of the classroom teacher, Socratic questioning, audio-visual aids, the use of the library and museum resources, laboratory practice, work experience. Some of these techniques are designed merely to transmit knowledge: to make available to the person seeking guidance the factual information necessary to his decision.

Others are designed to teach him the procedures of making choice, the methods of logical reasoning the canons of aesthetic discrimination the ethics of moral decision. Still others may be techniques to induce tranquillity of spirit, and produce social adjustment, mental health, or personal development. These techniques in turn may be either preventive or therapeutic.

There is also the field of vocational guidance, one of the most important of the traditional specialization. It has now been divided and subdivided so that there are vocational guidance experts who specialize on individual industries, and others who are experts on one stratum only of personnel, for example, 'middle management development'—there are even some who specialize on advising on the specific management courses which are most suitable for industrial executives within such a stratum. Specialization, however, has not limited itself to areas of interest, such as vocational, educational, or remedial. It has identified itself also, with institutions and age levels. Thus, there is the elementary school guidance officer, the home room guidance teacher, the specialist in reading clinics, the residence-halls expert, the juvenile court guidance officer, the clinician connected with an institution for the abnormal, and a dozen other categories. Within these areas there is beginning to grow up a sort of super specialization in the form of functional experts-the technician skilled in psychological tests, interview techniques, religious counselling, family life and marriage counselling, or inter-group relations.

It is perhaps inevitable hat with the growth of specialization and all the technical trapping of tests and techniques, there should develop a vigorous and at times militant professional movement. Priests have been advising adherents and parents have been guiding their children since prehistoric times, and on the record they have not done too badly. Teachers who themselves tend to be belligerently professional on occasion, have used many, if not most, of the recognised guidance techniques for centuries. There is one powerful school of though in the profession which feels the most guidance responsibilities should be centred in the classroom teacher, since only he can adequately known the individual from daily contact. But there is an equally powerful school which maintains that guidance is far too intricate to be permitted to any but the trained and presumably licensed specialist. The potential danger of bad advice has been widely recognized for some time, and the complexity of some of the esoteric techniques currently used by clinical guidance technicians is not to be denied. But the degree of mystery in which the whole process has been wrapped by enthusiastic participants is hardly warranted by the facts. One of America's leading educators, in commenting upon the speed with wh ich the field of guidance has been developing, wrote, "Like the Red Queen, you have to run as fast as you can to stay in the same place". Perhaps guidance, like religious conversion, or tribal initiation, or some forms of psycho-analysis, has to be experienced in order to be understood, and perhaps it is developing so rapidly that intelligent laymen cannot understand current advance. But the evidence does not appear to support either contention.

It is almost certainly due to this growth of professional vested interest that there has been created in the educational world something which might be termed guidance with a big 'G'. In the western countries especially in USA, there has grown up an attitude of possessiveness which at times is a little disconcerting. Thus, it is sometimes held that guidance is really only that which is traditionally considered to be guidance in the educational system. This comes perilously close to a definition of guidance as "those functions which the trained guidance official performs". More than once an American-trained guidance specialist has categorically dismissed the efforts of a foreign educational system with the sweeping generalization-"No guidance process exists." Nothing could be farther from the truth. Guidance exists, almost by definition, in every educational system, and in the vast majority of human relations. But it may both exist in forms which are familiar to a specialist preoccupied with tests and records and interview techniques and professional attitudes. To an unfortunately large number of American guidance technicians the counselling efforts of a typical British public school head master appear appealingly old-fashioned, slipshod and non-objective. But the educator knows that the very essence of the head master's task is guidance. The confusion, however, is more than merely a difficulty in semantics. It stems from the mistake of identifying the guidance process with currently fashionable techniques of collecting and systematizing the information which is considered useful in the process.

The inescapable truth is that the most distinguished guidance has always been that imparted by the world's greatest teachers—by the Christ walking with his disciples near the Sea of Galilee, by a Confucius writing his Analects, by a Machiavelli instructing his Prince, or by a parent rearing his child. Every person who succeeds in guiding another utilizes elements which appear indispensable. He must know the individual whether by scientific testing or by the apperception which comes from intimate daily contact. He must know the cultural setting, and in particular, those areas specifically interesting to the individual, whether he amasses vast files of sociological data, or whether he gets it by the intuitive understanding of a sensitive participant in life's activities. He must have a world view, a Wellanschauung, a comprehensive philosophy, which enables to correlate particular aspects of the individual's problem with the wider significance of social trends and ideal. He must have a certain humility as, through the instrument of his suggestion, he sets loose forces whose results he may not foresee. He must be a man of honour, who lives by the ethics acceptable to himself, to the individual seeking help, and to society. Some would add that these ethics must above all satisfy the profession, and perhaps they must where professional guidance is used. But for the rest, the criterion of a sympathetic heart, of a deep humanity, must suffice.

Finally, these guidance people whether they be professionals trained in universities, or devoted amateurs learned in the ways of men, must have the power of communicating with those they would help. With some it will be a coldly analytical transmittal of data or logical persuasion. With others only the receptive ear, sympathetically noting the pent-up urges of the individual, gently guiding him into safer, more desirable channels. But all must give to the individual the sense of their willingness and ability to help.

SEARCH FOR A DEFINITION OF GUIDANCE

Thus, there is much overlap between the connotation of the terms 'education' and 'guidance'. In all human societies guidance has been provided, but the agencies through which it has operated have changed and are changing. So are the problem-areas with which guidance is concerned.

At about this stage in our editorial thinking, we attempted to frame a definition of 'guidance' so as to focus the efforts of our contributors. We said : The word 'guidance' is used to denote efforts deliberately organized by groups to direct their members towards desired patterns of behaviour-desired because they are considered good either for the group as a whole, or for both. Guidance may be general and informal through agencies like the family, the Church, the school, the political party. It is carried on by procedures such as example, admonition, imitation, participation. In advanced and complex societies, it becomes increasingly specific in nature and is then the responsibility of experts. We wish to distinguish between 'guidance' and 'influence' and 'teaching', though both of the latter may be used as guidance procedure."

This attempt quite failed to secure the approval of those we consulted. As a result of many discussions we therefore proposed a fresh 'working definition'. Guidance, we said, is "a process of helping individuals through their own efforts to discover and develop their potentialities both for personal happiness and social usefulness."

Our later definition was, without doubt, an improvement on our first attempt. It suffered, however, from a great drawback. It might be taken to denote a corpus of knowledge, a set of techniques, a social control, a fad, a professional movement or, in fact, the whole of education. So we had to limit the scope of our treatment by applying severe criteria of exclusion.

First, there was a criterion of degree. We have attempted to present in this *Year Book* a panorama of services, techniques, and theories which are of general interest to guidance personnel connected with organized education as well as to all teachers. Efforts have been made to avoid massive detail which would enable the professional psychologist or guidance officer to do his job better.

Next, there was a criterion of extension. There are four broad areas of behaviour-influencing factors. These are : (a) entirely unformalized and non-institutionalized factors which influenced behaviour and attitudes, (b) commercially and politically instigated propaganda or advertising designed to guide persons in choice of products or in political allegiance, (c) the whole area of negative guidance, and (d) the consideration of guidance by restraint or compulsion.

Finally, there was a criterion of reference. It is repeatedly indicated that guidance is a process which reflects a social philosophy and the culture in which it is located. We have attempted to record in this volume the important characteristics of a particular type of guidance which we believe to be applicable to free and thinking men in a free and fundamentally democratic world. Where we have dealt with systems of guidance in areas which do not fully attain these standards, we have done so in the hope and belief that even in the most totalitarian society the individual does retain some measure of choice. We have seen the processes of guidance through eyes conditioned by our own freedom. Our working definition of guidance itself reveals a philosophical commitment to freedom and self-direction. We hold that the individual has the fundamental right to make choice which are neither efficient nor in his own best interests. And we deny that society has the right to impose upon the individual certain choice, merely for the sake of an efficiency which he or family reject. In adopting this position we as educators, reveal that we work within the frame of reference of a philosophy which protects the rights of minorities and elevates the individual to a position of importance which in some thing comes above that of the State.

CONCLUSIONS

1. The Spreading of Professionalized Guidance Services

From the monographs collected in this *Year Book* four general conclusion emerge quite clearly. The first is that professionalized guidance services are everywhere being established and are spreading chiefly because important and necessary functions are no longer effectively discharged by traditional agencies. The profound changes that are going on in the occupational structure, in the structure of the family, in habits and mores, in religion and ideology and in political situation-all these make it abundantly clear that the older, informal modes of providing guidance are failing to meet current needs or, even, breaking down altogether; so that there are good reasons for intensive study, for the activities of professionally trained specialists, and for structuring the whole business more coherently.

Let take an instance: adolescents in western societies feel a need for the guidance given by older and wiser persons. This was at one stage provided in english boarding schools by the head master or the house master, who knew the boy and his parents and was acquainted with their background and financial position, with the occupational opportunities available, the social codes in vogue, and so on. Nowadays, secondly grammar schools in England, as in U.S.A., have become mass institutions so that teachers hardly know more than the names of their pupils-who in any case are drawn from all ranks and classes. In these circumstances, is it strange that a specialist should be put in charge of guidance or that special techniques for gathering information about the young person being guided should be devoted? There is here no question about 'imitating other western countries', but rather of reacting to a situation which inhabitants encountered earlier than others.

2. Changing Role of the Secondary School in the Guidance Process

Traditionally, one of the aims of the secondary schools in days gone by was to provide guidance in the affairs of life by developing the power of reason and then showing how it could be applied to human affairs. But, however magnificent it may be, this ideal is not one which the secondary school of modern industrial societies can easily accept as attainable. One may say, indeed, that to pursue it in this twentieth century is to chase a will-o'the-wisp. For the new mass secondary schools are, rather characteristically, institutions which assist the total mobilization of the population for social and industrial ends. By their very structure, the school systems allocate the young into occupational groups and guide or even direct them towards accepted objectives.

In its modern form, the guidance given by school system seems to accept the notion that there are basic innate differences between individuals. It seems to be assumed that according to their capacities they can be fitted into their correct niche. Justice, happiness, social harmony, and efficiency depends on finding the right place for the right person. The basis of 'guidance' is then thought of in terms of (a) discovering the aptitudes and capacities of each individual and then, (b) placing him in society in such a position that he will be socially useful and happy. The vast number of specialisms today makes such a task extremely difficult. In some educational systems, like that of England, three broad groups are still being thought of and initial selection is in terms of these groups. England differs in this from many countries only in the early age (11+) at which the broad selection takes place. There is increasingly a process of further differentiation as pupils go through the educational system. At each stage the range of information imparted becomes smaller but-so it seems-its depth in increased. Having completed a course of formal education the student may find himself qualified only for a very limited range of occupation. On the other hand, if his education has been rather broader, he may find himself competing-to his disadvantage-with others who have had a more specialized training.

We have here an illustration of the way in which guidance may be provided by structuring a situation. The school system of a country is such that children are guided into different streams and there presented with specific life possibilities. If they do not fit into the ordinary categories, because they are too bright or too dull, special forms of guidance are provided, such as schools 'for handicapped until they learn to adapt themselves. Social control is applied, while an illusion of personal choice may persist.

3. GUIDANCE IS CONDITIONED BY SOCIAL ASSUMPTIONS

The most basic conclusion to be drawn from the material gathered in this Year Book, and one on the importance of which we cannot insist too much, is that 'guidance' is always deeply conditioned by the assumptions made by those in charge of the process. This conclusion may be unpalatable, since many technicians are convinced that they keep themselves entirely out of the business, leaving perfect freedom to their clients. Our statement, therefore, needs elucidation.

Let begin by asking about an individual whose mental health and tranquillity of spirit seem to demand a course a action which is normal, antisocial, or politically treasonable. The brilliant scientist who disclosed his nation's atomic secrets to an unfriendly power is a spectacular case in point. Such an individual, undeniably same in the legal sense, is driven to a course of action which is unacceptable to the society in which he lives. Yet this course seems essential to his peace of conscience in the murky half-light of his view of world peace. If such an individual should seek guidance from a counsellor prior to his treasonable act, what would be the advice given? Would it be truly non-directive, neutral in its morality, uncommitted in its political allegiance? Obviously not-for complete neutrality in guidance would be a denial in terms. Yet, if the guidance process is to be politically biased, if it is to take sides and attempt to lead the client to a specific decision, then it has ceased to be solely a technique, a method, and has become an end, a goal. What this goal will be is inevitably conditioned by the total culture, and hence guidance becomes in the end still another thing-a social control. It is not of importance that the example just given happens to be lurid and extreme. It would apply equally if the guidance were to help rehabilitate a juvenile deliquent or to prevent adolescent gang activity, or to channel youthful energies into 'proper' activities, or to build democratic loyalties, or combat the excesses of competitiveness or social consciousness. For in each, there has come into play some cultural standard or norm, a moral choice has been made.

What is 'guidance' then, as a social control ? It is surely an instrument for the achievement of some ideological goal or other. Thus, in the example just cited, the 'guidance' may incite the troubled scientist to betray his country on the grounds that he will then make a contribution to the dream of a world social revolution, or it may restrain his treason on the grounds of nationalism and patriotism, or perhaps it may invoke religious sanctions against his broken oaths. But whatever the specific direction of the counselling, such guidance acts as a social control since it specifically guides the subject into a socially accepted pattern, into a path of action and a set of attitudes which are determined by social organization and mores. And all this remains perfectly true even when the 'guide' or counsellor eschews all temptation to use authority or to issue directives.

Even when he merely helps his client, to discover the semi-conscious pre-judices or habits latent in his mind, leaving the ultimate decision absolutely to him, doing no more than helping the person in trouble to understand himself, even then the mores and the society come into action. There is, in truth, no absolutely 'non-directive' guidance, however one may try to create it. Guidance in a Communist society could not conceivably be the same as guidance in a Fascist society, and none of these could be called guidance in a democracy or in monarchic society.

4. General Trends in Guidance

In identifying trends which appear to represent the best current thought and practice within the profession, Professor Ruth Strang mentions four.

The first is a trend towards more participation by teachers in the guidance programmes, a reversal of the former policy of restricting the guidance activities to trained professionals. In this there seems to be a recognition of the importance of continued and daily contacts with the person seeking guidance and a lessening of the emphasis on difficult testing techniques and clinical methods.

The second is a trend towards development guidance. This is in part an effort to apply the guidance process to the whole personality of the individual rather than to fragmented elements such as his vocation, health, education, etc. In part too it is an effort to continue the process through the years so that the individual receives help when he needs it and in manner which is consistent with his physical and social maturation.

The third is a trend towards client-centered counselling. This was recognised as basic from the first planning of the volume, and is included in the working definition adopted. But in the sense that Professor Strang uses it, client-centred counselling includes not only a social context of freedom and self-direction, but also newly developed techniques which are presumed to be helpful in achieving this goal. The guidance officer attempts to set the stage so that the client sees for himself the basic issues and makes his choice for himself-always from among socially acceptable perceived alternative. And prominent among the new techniques are non-directive counselling, permissive guidance activities, and various elements drawn from the field of group dynamics, such as shared leadership.

The fourth is a trend towards what Professor Strang calls the "team approach". In the complexity of modern life, few if any individuals are equipped to give adequate guidance in many fields or to collect information through many specialized techniques. This makes almost inevitable the use of various facilities, sometimes grouped in a clinic, sometimes drawn from various agencies of the community If the client is to achieve the desideratum of continuity in his relationship and coordination between the many behaviour conditioning agencies. It will be necessary to establish some unifying binding force. Fundamental of course, is a common and recognized social philosophy-so that, in different agencies and different times, the guidance process is not applied to conflicting and antagonistic ends.

Almost equally essential will be some systematic continuity in the service, the maintenance of record, the wise use of guidance information tempered by charity and controlled by professional ethics.

To this analysis, we would add one reflection. We have been impressed by the degree to which the experimental approach has been effective in discovering new and fruitful techniques, such as the various group and community methods of diagnosis and treatment. We are impressed too, by the way in which new insights gained by psychiatrists in remedial work throw light on the problems and difficulties of ordinary people. Here, as in surgery and in psychology, it seems that the study of the diseased and abnormal helps one to understand better the usual and normal.

In closing this brief examination of the guidance process in its relation to education today, one may well be puzzled at the apparent simplicity of the area which has been advanced as a new and important educational discipline. Here is no profound and esoteric corpus of knowledge to master. With one or two notable exceptions, the tests and techniques are relatively simple in theory, even though at time of questionable validity in practice. In the past the major emphasis has been placed on collecting and verifying the knowledge, and it is only relatively recently that the more important and more difficult technique of acting upon the knowledge has become the principal focus of attention. In the limited area of communication much has been done, and guidance officer is today better equipped to transmit to the student his analysis of the pertinent data, and even his evaluation of the intangible and emotional factors. Group techniques and counselling methods may be invoked and personal decisions taken by the client. These are influenced by the guidance leader, who is not and cannot be truly neural. Yet in theory, and largely in practice these techniques are not difficult to understand. But in spite of its apparent simplicity the new orientation is highly promising and may transform education.

Successful guidance depends upon a skill infinitely more difficult to acquire than formal techniques. It depends upto warmth of personality, a depth of humanity, and a breadth of personal experience which only the gifted few possess. These men, whether they be the 'Mr. Chips' of the English public school or the professionally trained technicians of the guidance clinic, will find their reward in the enriched lives of those they "help through their own efforts to discover and develop their potentialities, both for personal happiness and social usefulness.

8

THE NEED FOR GUIDANCE AND COUNSELLING IN PHYSICAL EDUCATION

Guidance, or counselling, as an idea, has a long history and in the educational tradition of all countries there are to be found notable attempts to define it and practice it. Plato said, there may well be an art whose aim would be to effect this very thing, the conversion of the soul in the readiest way; not to put the power of slight into the soul's eye, which already has it, but to ensure that, instead of looking in the wrong direction, it is turned they way it ought to be":-

(1) Nowadays we tend to think of guidance as "a process of helping individuals through their own efforts to discover and develop their potentialities for personal happiness and social usefulness". (2) Looked at in this way it may not be obvious in what way guidance differs from education itself, nor why the concept of guidance has become such an important one at the present time. Although guidance has to be distinguished from education, for it is only one aspect of educational activity, yet it comes close to being the central or cardinal aspect of it. It is one of the main themes of this article that education, as the means of growth of the individual person within a community of persons, succeeds in its aim only in so for it is informed throughout by the spirit of guidance.

It is in the emphasis on the individual in our definition of guidance that we find the clue to what distinguishes it as an educational activity in its own right, and a clue to why it is of vital importance today. Speaking of the hindrances which exist to the full development of the individual, some eminent researchers admits that: "the individual needs some specialized assistance in understanding the nature of these hindrances, as well as in discovering his own potentialities to meet them. The heart of guidance lies in providing the individual with this specialized help". (3) Thūs guidance is a specialized activity directed to helping individuals overcome their difficulties in personal development, and we may hazard the opinion that its contemporary significance derives essentially from the plight of the individual person in face the impersonal character of modern mass society and its every-increasing and changing demands upon him.

EVIDENCE OF THE NEED FOR GUIDANCE

This plight of the individual person in the modern world in plain to see, if we are prepared to look at modern life unflinchingly and with eyes undazzled by the great achievements of our scientific age. To accept this, it is unnecessary either to assert that the individual's plight is worse than in past ages, or to deny the immense benefits which applied science has brought and is bringing, for example, through material prosperity and the conquest of disease.

We are dealing with an absolute fact-the fact of stress, unhappiness and misery, manifested through social disruption, and maladjustments in personal and working life, and evidenced by the statistics for refugees and homeless persons, occupational unsettlement, divorce, children in need of care and protection, psychosomatic illness, neurotic and psychotic disorders, crime, and destructive and violent behaviour generally.

This under two of misery and maladjustment, found in all modern societies and not least in those in course of rapid transition to a modern condition, has its counterpart also in the aimlessness and inner emptiness of the lives of millions of ordinary people who are never ill in the ordinary sense, never offend against society and who in outward appearances are fully occupied—perhaps too fully and too feverishly occupied. Where leisure exists and is increasing, there is a great misuse of it or failure to use it constructively.

There is everywhere a great and increasingly conscious pressure towards conformity of life patterns, and towards the uncritical acceptance of ready made values and the political myths created by ruling groups. There is in brief a widespread failure by modern man to accept the challenge of his birthright to think and feel for himself, and to embrace constructively, but critically, his responsibilities and privileges as a citizen of the world. This is the familiar cry of every social critic and reformer of our age, but it is worth repetition if we go on to realize that this "failure" of modern man is a failure brought about by our social failure to understand the overwhelming nature of the task which the individual now faces, and to provide him with an education which will fit to carry it out.

Modern social life demands a level of personal maturity which the majority of mankind have not attained, and cannot attain without an education which sees as its central concern the nurture of the individual and understands what this nurture entails in terms of personal guidance.

Evidence for this educational failure is to be found in plenty by a study of educational systems themselves, and ironically, but inevitably, it is manifested most clearly precisely at those points where we can claim the greatest educational advances, namely in the ever-increasing provision of educational facilities for all the children of all the people, everywhere. Our vast and growing educational enterprises are vast in their administrative and external aspects, but from time to time we become vividly aware that there is a certain hollowness within, where as yet out efforts to enable our pupils to develop to maturity through the education they receive can claim only very modest success.

There is overwhelming testimony to be found in all countries, of the extent to which what we offer, in the way we offer it, is unsuited to a very large proportion of our children. This appears most readily when we examine the gap between our alleged standard and the genuine achievements of children, and when we discover for example the proportion of the children admitted to our academic secondary schools who are unsuccessful in their studies when judged by the examination standards set up by these schools themselves to symbolize their aims. In England itself nearly forty percent of grammar school entrants leave without securing a worthwhile general certificate of education (4). The most damaging revelation, however, comes when we contrast examination success with the extent to which those who succeed in these examinations have progressed in acquiring the basic arts of living, as distinct from a mere knowledge of "subject". Knowledge is increasing at an alarming rate and we can show how our pupils are becoming increasingly stuffed with it at all levels up to and including the universities, but evidence to show that it is being effectively transmuted into what Whitehead called "active wisdom" is much harder to come by.

CAUSES OF EDUCATIONAL FAILURE

It is possible to point outside the school to many causes of difficulty and failure in the personal development of modern man. The vastness and speed of social change, and its disruptive effects on the traditional means of personal growth and nourishment is the most general cause, with the breakdown of the traditional family unit and the growth in complexity of occupational opportunity as its most general effects. In this situation the adolescent particularly is exposed to conflicts and perplexities with which we have not equipped him to deal. With the increasing emancipation of women and the spread of coeducation, a set of specially perplexing factors is added. But it is idle to blame our changing society, for such change has come to stay as a permanent feature of modern life and it is the task of the school to answer the challenge which it presents.

When we look within the school itself we can at once see some of the ways in which we are failing to meet the challenge and to some extent, as has been noted, these appear to be the direct result of our greatest efforts to expand educational provision and raise educational standards. There is the atmosphere of intense competition to be found both in the primary school, and in the academic secondary schools, particularly in Wester countries. Only the fittest survive this pressure and practically none survive it emotionally undamaged. There is the tremendous emphasis on standardized attainment, which tends to neglect the varying needs, temperaments and abilities of individual children. Above all there is the growing impersonality of the school itself, particularly as it become a bigger and more comprehensive unit-an impersonality also exaggerated, particularly at the primary stages, by the large size of classes. At the secondary stage one important factor making for impersonality and lack of concern for the child as an individual, and particularly as whole individual, is the organization of secondary work around subjects. Some organization of this kind is inevitable, but its effect is that teachers are more and more forced to be teachers of subjects rather than of children. And it is very rarely that a Head is in a position to know well even a majority of the pupils.

It could perhaps be said that the essence of this modern problem lies in the fact of the loosening and weakening of the personal environment of home and community outside the school, taken in conjunction with the relative failure to provide an educational environment within the school which is capable of supplying the missing personal nourishment. The nourishment needed is essentially to be thought about in terms of personal relationships, and of the guidance which springs out of such relationships, and it is here therefore within the school that we find the imperative need to develop our guidance and counselling services.

GUIDANCE WITHIN THE SCHOOL

The tendencies toward intense competition, standardized achievement and impersonality which are now prominent features of all our educational system, can be counteracted in the first instance only by the creation of an effective special guidance and counselling service within the schools themselves. Such services, of course, already exist in many places, but they are still mainly in the embryo stage. The U.S.A. may perhaps be cited as an exception, but while what has happened there is a potent, it is not necessarily an example to be followed elsewhere. Each country must develop means suited to its own educational situation and aims. While the creation of a special guidance service within schools is a necessary step, it is by itself by no means a sufficient one.

On the one hand it has to be related to the still more specialized services both clinical and vocational outside the school, which are becoming more and more recognized as essential ancillary agents of the educational system. On the other hand, a guidance service within the school must be supported by the whole of the school, and its existence, if it does its work well, must necessarily in time come to modify the school's whole approach to its educational function.

What are the special duties of a guidance officer or counsellor, for example within a large secondary school? Ideally he should have a major say in working out the course to be followed by each child, whether the organization permits only of guidance by "classification" into streams or sets or whether it permits guidance of a much more fundamental and individual kind. He should have the surveillance of the teaching of the more backward and difficult children and should do some of this teaching himself. By his role he is also ideally fitted to carry out that aspect of vocational guidance which is the proper function of the school, and in doing this he must establish sound relationships with all those community agencies which interest themselves in job placement and the welfare of young people after leaving school. He must also be closely linked with the area's clinical services and be ready to call on specialized psychological aid when this is necessary. Not least, he must, wherever necessary and possible, establish relations with parents. But above all, he must be a person in the school who by virtue of his unique role and special skills is naturally and at need consulted by staff and also by pupils. His door must be always open to everyone. It is specially important that he acts always as a guide and consultant, and that he himself does not take executive action. Executive power must remain with the Head of the school, and with the teaching staff under his direction. This is quite fundamental. It is fundamental that the Head and staff should retain their authority.

The counsellor must never usurp their functions. Not only would such action be intolerable for them, it would also destroy the counsellor's own role which ultimately depends on his not being a wielder of authority, a judge of right and wrong. Just how fundamental this point is will appear in a moment.

It will, however, be obvious that the work of the counsellor will depend absolutely on the degree of co-operation he can obtain from Head and staff. On the teaching staff he must rely for much of his information and in turn they must be prepared to give sympathetic consideration to his views, if his work is to count for anything. In order to do this they must begin to understand something of his work and approach. In fact it is to be hoped and indeed expected (if he is successful) that through his influence, his attitude and the needs of his job, there will in time come about a subtle change in the attitude of teaching staff to their roles as educators. In the case of any given child, the counsellor's interventions are bound to be episodic, but one of the essentials of effective guidance is its continuity. Such continuity can only be attained if the guidance attitude comes to permeate the work of the school as a whole, and thus comes to re-fashion the relations between teachers and pupils. It is for this reason that the creation of a specialized guidance service within a school cannot be a complete answer to the need for guidance.

Ultimately all educators must come to see their supreme function as that of guides to the growing person, not only in relation to learning in the school sense but to the wider learnings which mark his growth to maturity. Within the school itself the essential change that is needed is the development of a view of education which sees the acquisition of knowledge and skills as only means towards the growth of persons to maturity. Emotional and social development them become primary aims of education. Clearly, if special guidance and counselling services are to become effective educational instruments in spreading the spirit of guidance, the training of the teachers of the future must seek above all things to secure the development of those attitudes towards education which lie at the heart of the guidance function.

THE ESSENCE OF GUIDANCE

It is only too easy to suppose that the essential skills of the counsellor or of the teacher who approaches education in the spirit of guidance are mainly those manipulative skills derived from technical developments in the field of psychological measurement and assessment. Children are tested and assessed and their educational environment is fashioned or re-fashioned to suit their needs. Such work is a necessary part of guidance, but it is only the outer husk. It is that part of guidance which may be called "contrivance" (5) through which the external stresses and strains to which the individual is subjected may be modified. The kernel of guidance however lies in the relationship which the counsellor establishes with his clients and through which they are enabled to develop further their own powers of dealing with both inner and outer problems. It is not so much what he does, but what he is to them, and enables them to do, which is important. It is their inner freedom, their own understanding, their powers of decision and of embracing purposes of their own, which have to be strengthened.

The essential skills of guidance therefore lie within the counsellor's or teacher's own personality, in the extent of his insight into the problems and conflicts which beset the growing person, and which for him were first exemplified in his own growth to maturity. His first and most fundamental need is to understand himself and the relation in which he stands to children. If the relationship is to nourish their growth, it is essential that he becomes to some extent the ally of the child's own ego, the central part of his personality, rather than of the child's moral function or superego, to use Freud's term. It is difficult for the teacher to establish this relationship in any strength-but it can be done-all "good" teachers achieve it. Generally the teacher functions most readily as an external or ancillary super-ego for the child, in the same way as his parents did in his early years. It is fundamentally in this sense that the teacher is a parent substitute-a source of authority. The teacher can not but embody many aspects of authority for the child, no matter how "permissive" and non-authoritarian he may be, but he can also establish himself as a guide or friend, who seeks to understand rather than to judge, just as, and even more easily than the good parent can. The counsellor, by virtue of his special role, is in a position to maximise the extent to which he appears to the child as someone who will always befriend him, and to minimise the extent to which he appears as only an additional figure in authority over him. It is for this reason that the counsellor should not assume executive functions. The counsellor's role is therefore a difficult one and calls for special personal qualities-qualities which all good teachers must possess, but which the counsellor must and can exemplify to a especially high degree.

While our perception of the need for guidance in education may at first arise from a consideration of the external complexities of modern society, an understanding of the real nature of this need cannot be reached unless we perceive that the essential problem is the nourishment of those powers of the individual by virtue of which he becomes more able to withstand the pressures, external (the opinions and exhortations of others) and internal (his own feelings) which beset him, and more able to take his destiny into his own hands. It is only as individuals can progressively come to master their own passions and fears, and to command their powers of rational thought and decision, that they can enter into fruitful and cooperative relations with one another. Otherwise these relations become distorted through outward duress and/or inner compulsion. We have therefore to look to a form of guidance in education which seeks to help the individual to achieve his own maturity, as one of the essential means by which men may eventually grow out of this age of anxiety and confusion and lay claim to their birthright of rational freedom.

9

THE ROLE OF PSYCHOLOGICAL GUIDANCE IN NATIONAL PLANNING

Though, India has received the political independence but yet we are often reminded that we have a long way to go yet. Achievement of political freedom was the first step. Economic and social freedom has still to be acquired. To attain this end national planning has been adopted as the means. We seem to believe in five-year periods of attempts. We have made one such effort and are in the midst of the second. The emphasis in the first plan was on food. In the second, it is on industry, particularly on the heavy variety.

One of the essential requirements of industrial development is technically trained manpower. We are short of technicians and engineers. To overcome this difficulty new Institutes of Technology are being opened. The number of Engineering Colleges is being increased and the training capacity of the existing institutions is being enlarged.

But how are we to find the lads who are to go into these institutions? By selection from those available? "Yes" seems to be the answer to this question. But selection presupposes abundant supply of suitable people. If the supply is less than the demand the question of selection does not arise. One has to take what one gets and be content with it. To produce an abundant supply for technical training institutes Psychological Guidance in schools will be found of service. To find out the potentialities of young people and to guide them into suitable vocations is the essence of Psychological

Guidance. An extensive School Psychological Service will contribute substantially to the successful completion of the National Plans.

In the present economic context of our country it will be wise to broaden the concept of guidance. Normally guidance is understood to mean the finding out of the youth's potentialities by Psychometric and projective Tests, Questionnaires and Interview and telling him what particular vocation he is best suited for. It will be helpful to include counselling also under the term guidance. I feel it is necessary in the present economic and social setup of the country.

It is needed to remove the prejudices and widen the vision of the youth. There is still a prejudice amongst us against working with hands. We still want white-collar jobs. We are averse to putting on dirty overalls, soiling our hands and sweating while we work. The prejudice is unconsciously passed on to the youth. Majority of the young lads, found suitable for technical training, are desirous of becoming engineers. They are shy of being workmen even though their potentialities do not promise them anything better.

Prejudice against working with hands holds them back. Most of them ultimately drift into offices to become inefficient and discontented clerks. Counselling, if properly done, will help to remove the prejudice and will, perhaps, be successful in diverting a large number from the army of clerks to the army of technically trained workmen who are so urgently needed for the success of our plans.

It is not enough to tell the young boy what particular job he is best suited for. Our diagnosis tells him where he will be successful. But we have to be careful and prepare him for failure also. By telling the boy that he will make a good engineer we are perhaps raising his hopes. Under the present, conditions it is quite possible that the he may not be able to secure admission in an Engineering College. That means frustration- a frustration greatly intensified by the consciousness that he has the potentiality of becoming a good engineer. Unfortunately, the number of such young people is quite large under the present state of unemployment in the country. A large body of frustrated youth is more likely to hinder than to help the successful completion of the plan. It is true that the plan itself is trying to remove unemployment, but it is going to take a long time before this objective is achieved.

Unemployment will exist in the country for some time to come, and the youth will continue to be frustrated. Frustration in youth, followed by a negative attitude and antisocial activities, could be fought by Psychological Guidance. This can best be done by counselling. Through counselling the young people should be taught to face defeat and not to lose their mental balance in the struggle for employment. They could be encouraged to start at a lower rung of the ladder and work their way up. If they have potentialities of being successful at the top, those very potentialities will help them to rise quicker. What they require is patience, and patience is better than frustration. Counselling, therefore, seems to be urgently needed to be included in the technique of guidance.

If our plans have to be successfully completed we will have to have enthusiastic young men. No matter how good the plan, if we have diffident and frustrated young men to work it the result is obvious. We have to produce self-confidence and enthusiasm in the youth. Psychological Guidance can help to achieve this aim. But the concept of Guidance must be widened. It has a heavy mathematical bias at present. If it is to help national planning it must include a little more Psychology.

10

THE ROLE OF GUIDANCE AND COUNSELLING IN MANPOWER PLANNING

Before the industrial revolution, which really began with the invention of the steam engine, the social and economic life of all countries was much simpler than it is today. The population of the world was smaller, the tempo of life much slower and space had not been conquered by modern methods of travel. To a large extent, the life of the average person was dominated by the conditions in his immediate environment and such population and occupational adjustments as had to be made could usually be achieved within each locality. Of course, what has been said is a generalization to which there was inevitable exception, but it is certainly true that in those earlier and more leisurely days, the need for manpower planning was practically nil.

This last century, however, has brought a complete revolution in the life of mankind. Space and time have been shortened enormously. The tempo of life has increased. Populations now uninhibited in their growth as a result of modern system of medicine, better nutrition and a more varied and interesting life, have grown enormously. At the same time thousands of new occupations have been created, with the result that manpower planning has become an essential part of a well-organized society.

Manpower planning like any other form of planning is an adjustment of supply and demand. In this case it is a process whereby the essential characteristics and abilities of the population are studied in detail and related to or adapted to the day-to-day manpower requirements of modern society. In a vague way the need for this has been appreciated for some years, but only more recently, as the complexity of modern economic life has grown, and as the number of occupations into which individuals can enter has increased, has the need for detailed manpower planning become imperative. Great strides are being made in this direction in all countries and India is by no means lagging behind.

In fact, quite a number of foreign observers who have come in contact with those engaged in manpower planning in this country have commented very favourably and with some surprise on the techniques and methods which are being adopted to develop manpower planning programmes. It is against this background that we must consider the role of guidance and counselling in manpower planning.

It will be readily realized that manpower planning, however good it may be, will prove quite infructious unless there are agencies capable of turning the manpower plan into a reality in terms of human aspirations and abilities.

A manpower plan will fail unless it not only appeals to the imagination of the people, but is also able, demonstrably, to give happiness and satisfaction to the average citizen. It is not an over-simplification to say that the average human being is not very hard to please and to make happy. The needs of most of us can be stated in fairly simple terms. Our first need is perhaps a sense of security; freedom from want, freedom from fear in our social and political relationships, and freedom from sickness. Another strongly felt need of the average man is the need to feel what we are doing is worthwhile. Another elementary desire of most of us is the desire to continually better ourselves, economically, socially and intellectually. In other words, whatever may be the manpower or economic plan of a country, it should set out to meet these elemental requirements of the average individual. Human beings are not and should not be pawns in political, social and economic games, and it is at this point that there is need to develop sound systems of vocational guidance and counselling.

It is axiomatic that no two human beings are alike, each one of us differs in physical, intellectual and social attributes. We are all motivated by different impulses, physical, psychological and intellectual and the aim of those responsible for guiding us should be to ensure that at a young age, our feet are set on a road which will lead to the maximum use of all our abilities and characteristics.

Square pegs must go in square holes, round pegs in round holes and all the other intermediate shapes suitably adapted. This is the ideal and, as the reader will readily realize, it is an ideal which it will probably take a long time to achieve. The encouraging thing is that the need for such achievement is being increasingly recognized. Evidence of this is to be found in the development of vocational and educational guidance and counselling and the interest being taken in the welfare of workers.

Despite the difficulty of the task before us, there are several obvious lines of development which can be fairly readily taken up. For instance, India's rapidly developing industrial life will require more and more engineers, craftsmen and technicians during the years to come. Among our many millions of population, there will be tens of thousands of young people whose aptitudes, inclination and physical characteristics make them more suitable for such work than their contemporaries. The task of the vocational guidance worker and counsellor is to acquire detailed knowledge of the task to be performed and to locate those of our young people who have the necessary aspirations, aptitudes and abilities to take up such work. Similarly, our need to bring education to all our people will require, during the coming years, an estimation of the number of educationists required for the purpose. It is for those concerned with manpower planning to estimate the numbers required and suggest the phasing of the programme. When that has been done it is for those who are engaged in educational and other forms of guidance to locate those of our young people most suited for this work. The nature of the task to be done and the characteristics which are essential for a teacher or a professor are vastly different from those required of an engineer, a craftsman or a technician. The difference in characteristics, abilities and aptitudes are capable of analysis and it is to this task that those engaged in guidance and counselling should direct their activities. What has been said of engineers, craftsmen, technicians, and educationists, is not less true of all other occupations which go to make up the complex society in which we live.

From what has been said it will be seen that a good deal of basic study has yet to be done if our objectives are to be achieved. At present for instance, very little is yet known about our occupational life. Before we can utilize any utilize any conclusions with regard to the abilities or aptitudes of individuals, we must have a far clearer picture of the jobs which have to be filled. It is for this reason that the Government of India, in the Ministry of Labour and Employment, is busily at work preparing not only an occupational classification, but also an analysis and description of each job which is commonly performed in the country. Having got this information it is then essential to make the material readily available to those who are responsible for giving guidance and counselling both to young people and to adults together with estimates of the numbers required.

This is being done by producing and distributing career pamphlets and information about careers and trainings facilities in the country. It is only when our young people are in a position to readily read about a variety of occupations that they will be able to make an intelligent choice of a career. Even then they will need wise counsel from their teachers, their parents, their Employment Officers and their friend so that they can match, realistically, their ambitions and aspirations with their abilities.

It is perhaps, desirable at this point to sound a word of warning. Although Vocational and Educational Guidance and Counselling are given a precise connotation by various experts, it needs, perhaps, to be recognized that, however good might be a system of Vocational Guidance and Counselling through the medium of experts, their activity cannot be a substitute for the collective wisdom of society as represented by, shall we say, parents, friends, relatives, teachers, the writers of books and magazines and the press. All these agencies are continually giving guidance good, bad or indifferent, to young people. It is important, therefore, that all these agencies must, of necessity, become increasingly enlightened, if each succeeding generation of young people is to quickly reach vocational maturity and make sound choices of careers.

It is also no less desirable to emphasize that because each one of us in an individual and will never cease to be so, it is essential that in the last analysis it is for each boy or girl, to make his or her own choice of career, whatever may be the wishes of those engaged in manpower planning, education of vocational guidance or counselling. Guidance should lead to self-choice.

Despite what I have said above, however, it can hardly be disputed, in view of very widespread ignorance, conservatism, prejudice and lack of knowledge of the basic facts of our social and economic life, that there is need for the development of specialized services through which expert guidance can be given to our young people. Such services will, it is hoped, set an example to the community as a whole. It is to be hoped, therefore, that there will be a rapid increase in the number of teachers in schools, who are specially trained to give guidance to school children. Similarly, it is desirable that at Employment Exchanges specially trained staff should be increasingly engaged in the task of helping employment seekers to make suitable occupational choices when they are looking for work. It is, for this reason that recent developments under the Central and State Governments to provide such expert guidance are being increasingly developed. Such agencies are essential collaborators with those engaged in manpower planning, and it is their role to endeavour that the guidance that they give is related, on the one side, to the essential manpower requirements of the country and on the other to the wholesome development and he achievement of contentment of each individual that comes to them.

11

THE IMPORTANCE OF OCCUPATIONAL INFORMATION PROGRAMME IN PHYSICAL EDUCATION

It has been estimated that every year some two million new people enter into the already over crowded employment market in India. In the beginning of the Second Five-Year Plan there were over five million people seeking employment. With the annual influx of two million additional men and women to the market the problem becomes so huge that it cannot be satisfactorily handled without the development of large-scale industries and without some kind of social and economic revolution.

Fortunately for us the social and economic revolution is taking place peacefully through the well-phased five-year plans. It is true that the unemployment problem has, in spite of all possible measures having been taken to halt it, continued to deteriorate, but it cannot be denied that the rate of deterioration has been checked.

According to a survey conducted in 1955-56, 154.84 million people were engaged in India in gainful employment. They included 110.61m. in agriculture, animal husbandry, etc.; 3.15 m. in factories; 94 m. in forestry, fisheries, etc.; 1.56 m. in railways and communications, 0.79 m. in mining, 10.18 m. in commerce including bank, insurance and transport, 7.56 m. in professions, in liberal arts, 3.50 m. in domestic services, 4.70 m. in Government services (administration) and 11.85 m. in small and cottage industries.

Besides this huge number of people engaged in work it is proposed that 6 million new employments would be created during the Second Plan period. A number of large-scale and small-scale industries are being established in different parts of the country. In the fields of social welfare, health, education, agriculture and horticulture, mining, new employment opportunities are being created. In the community development projects thousands of people will be required for rural upliftment work.

In spite of the development schemes that we have the available employment opportunities in the country when compared with the available manpower are hopelessly inadequate. That in itself is a serious problem. But besides this there is another important problem—the problem regarding dearth of facilities for occupational information necessary for employment seekers. It is true that due to slow progress in industrial development the number of occupation in our country is still much less than the number of occupations developed in other industrially developed countries.

In the United States 40,000 distinguishable occupations have been put on record. In the United Kingdom also where the people do not like to make hair-split distinctions in many cases between one occupation and another, it is estimated that 10,000 occupations exist. It our country industrial revolution has just started. Still there no less than 4,000 occupations from which a young man or woman may make a selection.

As the industry is growing and the scientific technology is developing old methods of work are being abandoned, old tools, implements and machines are being replaced with new ones and old techniques are giving way to modern ones. In this process new jobs are being created for new types of people who can learn new techniques of production and who can adjust themselves in new environments. These days when young men and women come out to make their choice of career they are confronted with numerous complicated problems. They do not know what occupations are suitable for them, where the suitable occupations are available, how to prepare themselves for those occupations and so on. Moreover, they like to know something about a number of occupations so that they may compare the prospect in all these occupations to avoid the risk of entering a blind alley job.

The selection of right occupation on the part of a new entrant in the world of work is important not only for him, but also for the management and the nation at large. It is a well-known fact that unless a worker gets maximum job satisfaction his output cannot be optimum. A worker can enjoy his work if he selects a career where he suffers neither from excessive strain on him nor from overplay of idle imagination.

With a view to help individuals to make judicious choice of careers, to assist parents and teachers to guide their children in going to the right field of work, to help employers to select persons who are conscious of the hazards and risks in their employment, several agencies both public and private are trying to disseminate objective occupational information to those who seek for it. Amongst the public agencies, it may be said that the Directorate General of Resettlement and Employment under the Ministry of Labour and Employment is the pioneer in this field. The D.G.R. and E. are collecting employment market information of the whole country through the network of Employment Exchanges and are publishing a series of Career Pamphlets on a very wide range of occupations.

In these pamphlets information is given on educational and physical requirements for the job, on place of work, training facilities, average income, future prospects, and employment outlook. Besides these, Youth Employment

Offices and Adult Counselling Centres have been opened in a number of big cities in the country to give occupational information to employment seekers. D.G.R. and E. publish Occupational Field Reviews and National Classification of Occupations which are of great value to any occupational information centre. The Handbooks on Training facilities in the State and the two volume of the Hand-books on Training Facilities in India are also considered to be unique publications in the country.

Education authorities are also, in a few cases, giving out some occupational information to school-leavers through talks on careers and through organized visits to industries and other places of work. The Ministry of Defence and the Ministry of Commerce and Industry also publish brochures and charts which contain valuable information on occupation in Defence Forces and in small-scale and cottage industries.

There are some private agencies which have made considerable contribution to the dissemination of occupational information to young people. Amongst them Y. M. C. A. Publishing House, Calcutta, Rotary Club, Bombay, Vocational Guidance Bureau, Bombay, and other Vocational Guidance Bureaux in the States are worth mentioning.

That the objective occupational information is of great value to a young person, when he is confronted with the problem of choosing a career, cannot be denied by anybody. The process of colleting, collating, and giving out the information, however, is very complex in a vast country like ours where development is uneven and occupations have not been standardized as yet. Some people think that useful occupational information on a national basis cannot be given at this stages as all the necessary data cannot be collected.

There may be some truth in this argument. Nevertheless, when partial information is collected from different parts of the country after watching some workers on the job, interrogating workers, supervisors, and instructors in industries and after going through relevant literature, it is bound to be useful to employment seekers. The agency that undertakes the collection of occupational information, however, takes all possible precautions to see that the field staff permit only minimum personal factor to play in their study of occupations. With these objects in view, training courses for field staff are organized and they are trained to sift out the useful and objective information on occupation.

There is no doubt that as the country progresses, more and more industries will be developed and more and more people will look for wage employment. The Occupational Information Programme will then have much more importance than what it has today. Their future is not very much distant. Occupational Information Programme, started recently in this country is still in the preparatory stage.

Those, who are trying to make the young people of the country careers conscious by disseminating objective occupational information in a scientific manner, are doing a great service to the nation. Those, who subscribe to the view that the Five-Year Plan can be saved by the Vocational Guidance Programme of which occupational information programme is the most important part, do not possibly exaggerate it.

(12)

THE SIGNIFICANCE OF PLANNING, PRINCIPLES, POLICIES, AND STANDARD PRACTICES IN PHYSICAL EDUCATION

THE ROLE OF PLANNING

The role of planning is to take action in the present that will influence the future. Administrators outline steps that must be taken to achieve the objectives that will advance the organization toward its goals. Planning precedes organizing and plays an important part in decision making. Policy planning, organizational planning, procedural planning, curricular planning and activity planning all have their own particular role descriptions and specific meanings.

Planning has been found to be important in the following ways:

- Sound and thorough planning tends to lessen the number of arbitrary actions. The path is clearly laid out.
- Systematic planning can help avoid role ambiguity and therefore role conflict.
- Effective planning with regard to salaries and fringe benefits can reduce dissatisfaction among the staff

and tends to diminish the number of arbitrary promotions and dismissals.

- The process of planning leads to more frequent reviews of current situations and subsequent maintenance, repair, or reconstruction.
- Careful planning will include meticulous care of records that contain objectives and goals. Perennial review of objectives and goals will do much to improve the entire operation.

Planning is essentially a special case of decision making with constant consideration of the future. Its basic steps are the same as those listed for problem solving. Planning has futuristic overtones. The final selection of any plan must be based on conditions and facts that are valid both today and tomorrow.

In every phase of the planning process, there are certain steps that must be included. These are the development of goals, objective, policies, procedures, and programs.

Obviously the size of the entire operation must be assessed. The basic fact on which everything else depends must be the enrolment, current and projected. The size of each class must be determined, the facilities to handle the projected enrolment considered, the financial resources carefully analysed, and the local and state rules and regulations thoroughly understood.

POLICIES AND STANDARD PRACTICES

Policies are essential to the efficient administration of any department, school, business, or other organization. Without them, there is little to guide the activities and conduct of the establishment in the pursuit of its goals. With well-reasoned policies, the organization can function efficiently and effectively, and its members will better understand what is expected of them.

Individuals are generally quite sensitive to treatment that they conserve discriminatory. They believe justice requires that the punishment be appropriate to the offence, that all persons be treated impartially, and that people should be informed about the behaviour expected of them. Goods laws are a part of the answer.

In any enterprise, it is important that the operation be efficient, and effective. Undue waste of time, money, and resources is deplored. Standard operating practices increase efficiency.

In educational institutions, as in other large organizations, some standardization is desirable. While individual differences should receive appropriate attention, correct and incorrect solutions and methods must be identified. Specific instruction and procedural requirements that are clearly spelled out result in a more productive organization.

System and organization, when not emphasized to the extreme, are to be preferred to anarchy and chaos. Authority, rightfully delegated or assumed, must be exercised if all efforts are to be coordinated and effective. Well-founded policies are helpful.

Many problems, tasks, and circumstances are repetitious. It is wasteful to spend time, energy, and resources to study them over and over again when a similar decision in each case is best. Suitable written guidelines help in economizing on time and energy.

To deal martially with people, to avoid waste of energy and resources, to bring about desirable standardization of procedures, to use what is learned in one instance to improve future decision, and to eliminate chaos, institutions establish and utilize guidelines of several kinds.

Depending upon the nature of the guidelines and the hierarchical level at which they are formulated and utilized, they are variously termed policies, standard procedures, standard practices, standard methods, guiding principles, rules, or just general guidelines. Well will use the terms policies, standard practices, and guidelines

THE NATURE OF POLICIES

A policy is a guiding principle that serves as a basis for a course of action. A policy does not spell out in detail exactly what is to be done, but it does point the direction. It should assist those who must make executive decisions, but it should not be so inflexible as to leave little latitude for individual judgment.

Policy making is often a major function of school committees, boards of trustees, athletic committees, and other legislative bodies. Policy may also be formulated and established at lower administrative levels. As one narrows the group to which they are addressed, finally coming right down to the individual, policies become more specific. As one ascends the hierarchical ladder or increases the scope of one's public, policies become more general.

It can readily be seen, then, that a policy might be formulated by a school committee, spelled out in a set of more specific statements by the superintendent of schools, and developed in even greater details by the athletic department. For example, a college board of trustees might establish a policy to the effect that "purchasing should be a centralized function". The president would then formulate a policy stating that all purchases should clear through the office of the controller.

The controller, in turn, would delegate the authority to select physical education equipment to the director of that department while establishing a policy stating that all requisitions must be countersigned in the controller's office. The director of physical policies and procedures relating to the selection and purchase of equipment.

STANDARD PRACTICES

A policies are promulgated and authority is delegated, one eventually arrives at the operating level. By this time, directions and guidelines have become so specific that they can no longer rightly be termed policies but rather standard practices or procedures.

Standard practices are rather specific instructions about how to proceed with a given task. Within the framework of established policies, a coach might be taking a track team on a trip. In a well-organized department, there would be specific guidelines about how many players could be carried, the maximum allowance for food, the method of accounting for expenditures, procedures for dealing with series injuries, and the conduct of athletes on trips, These and more would be spelled out in written standard practices or similar guidelines.

In many instances, it is difficult to determine just when instructions are policies and at what point they become standard practices. It is impossible to draw a hard and fast line. For this reason, some institutions prefer to use the term guidelines for their sets of instructions.

POLICIES AND PLANNING

It is impossible to separate policy formulation from planning, since it is, in fact, a very important part of planning. When goals have been established and directions determined, policies that guide that enterprise toward them should be formulated. Whenever a legislative or controlling body formulates a general statement of philosophy and direction, it is formulating policy.

At lower her archical levels, policy statements emerge when decisions are made about priorities in the use of facilities, criteria for salary increments, disciplinary measures for students, limits on faculty loads, requirements for graduation, guidelines for grades, or eligibility rules for athletes. Most of these are established in advance, and all of them are intended to guide future action. They are, then, an integral part of planning.

POLICIES AND DECISION-MAKING

Not all decisions can be based on established policies. Most situations have unique elements that require individual study and decisions appropriate to the particular circumstances. Nevertheless decisions should be made in light of policies that exist. If a pending decision is not compatible with an established policy, it should be studies carefully to determine whether or not the specific circumstances merit special consideration.

In many instances, the director of physical education and athletics is put in an intermediary position between his or her immediate superior or an established policy on the one hand and the athletes and/or coaches on the other. In such cases, decisions and actions will be strengthened by a firm policy and superiors who will back the director. Policies are often unpopular, but they are usually less objectionable than an arbitrary decision by one individual.

Executives responsible for athletic programs have a large number of difficult decisions to make. The eligibility of athletes, the recruitment practices of coaches, the interference by alumni, the emphasis on winning records, and the temptations to exploit athletes are potential trouble spots. Thoughtfully prepared policies and conscientious adherence to them will help the athletic director avoid many pitfalls.

In all institutions, some control over decision making is necessary. Defining the purpose of an organization, ensuring that decisions are guided by reason, prescribing lines of authority, and establishing guidelines are ways of accomplishing this.

POLICIES AND ORGANIZING

Organizing consists of grouping tasks and individuals related by common responsibilities. Without some guidelines, it is difficult to avoid duplication of effort, and without general principles, misunderstanding regarding duties and responsibilities are much more apt to arise.

As an example, policies, concerning the use of the gymnasium are essential. Such policies should indicate what the priorities are, who is the final authority in case of conflicts, where the master schedule is kept, and which activities should be scheduled during each hour of the day.

If coaches teach and teachers coach, there must be guiding policies for the division of labour, the manner of computing teacher local, and compensation for extra duty. There must also be a clear understanding about who reports to whom; otherwise two superiors may claim the same time for a given employee.

Policies should also cover use of funds. If the budget is to cover all activities, it is important that the sports with small spectator appeal be protected. Clearly defined relationships and carefully planned budgets will help. Departmental and program organization must also take into account the educational values for all the students. They should not be influenced unduly by dramatic appeals and popular demand.

Good communications system help executives in the process of coordination. They also assist managers who are striving to unite the work of different people in their efforts to achieve the objectives that have been developed for the organization. The success of any enterprise depends to a large extent on how well administrators organize individual tasks so that they are joined into a combined, purposeful action.

POLICIES AND DIRECTING OR COORDINATING

Policies, rightly used, are an effective way of communicating. Relevant and carefully formulated policies can serve as an effective means of directing. Inasmuch as the policies are generally disseminated to all units of an organization, they serve as coordinating devices as well as directives. They also speed up communications for they not only pass along the "channel of command" but they provide multiple channels by which message flow in all direction and to all units of the organization.

Few modern business, however, can tolerate having communication flow only through the channel of command. Each manager would be a potential bottleneck for the flow of essential information. The sheer mass of detail in most departments makes direct communication between operators necessary. Once an activity passes beyond the ability of a man to attend to every detail, routine and standard information must flow from one operator to another without managerial attention. An executive would be forced to neglect other duties if he tried to make himself the exclusive transmitter of information.

STANDARD PRACTICES, POLICIES, AND CONTROLLING

Controlling is the process of assessing performance and outcomes on the basis of established criteria. These criteria consist of hopes and plans articulated in the form of goals, policies, and standard practices. If the plans have been carefully laid, the policies thoughtfully formulated, and the standard practices meticulously followed, the results should approach or even exceed expectations. Policies and standard practices, in situations where the persons involved in implementation have also had an important role in their formulation, serve as guidelines and instructions for almost every phase of the operation. Individuals who feel that these were arrived at democratically and are soundly conceived will generally work energetically and enthusiastically to see that they are followed.

Basic policies in physical education and athletics should emphasize the key role of the student in education. The governing factor in many important decisions should be "the most good for the most students." This idea can be formulated as a statement of policy and can be used as a yardstick in the evaluation of the program. If inordinate attention is given the talented student, the great musician, or the star athlete, it may be noted as a weakness.

Disproportionate importance attached to special education for the handicapped, with too little energy and resources for other aspects of the program, will also be considered in the process of controlling. If he two extremes, the talented and the handicapped, are given so much consideration that there is little left for the middle eighty percent, this too will be seen as a flaw. If careful thought is given to the basic policy, all segments of the student body will receive consideration.

Personnel policies may include a statement to the effect that there will be no discrimination in employment or compensation on the basis of sex, race, or religion. Standard practices will spell out procedures for implementing that policy and evaluative steps for determining compliance.

A departmental policy may state that in the conduct of athletics the health and safety of the athletes are of primary concern. Standard practices may consist of instructions in case of injury and safety procedures to prevent accidents.

It becomes obvious that policies and standard practices are indispensable to the processes of evaluating and controlling and are necessary for a sound administration.

FORMULATING POLICIES

Preparing policies is an important task that is usually carried out at the administrative level. The dean of students is generally responsible for decisions regarding student life. The athletic director and the comptroller are both involved with regulations concerning the expenditure of money for team travel. Staff members responsible for other activities must likewise be included in the groups assigned to formulate policies for the conduct of those activities. Each committee engaged in writing policies and other regulations should include at least one member who has the ability to express ideas in a clear and concise manner.

All members of a policy-writing committee should be instructed to research all pertinent facts thoroughly before making their report to the organizational unit involved.

Well-written policies provide security to members of an organization. One of the chief causes of confusion in large organizations is the lack of clear-cut rules, regulations, and policies.

THE ADMINISTRATIVE HANDBOOK

Institutions and their subdivisions have found administrative handbooks (also referred to as policy books or administrative guides) both useful and effective. Smaller institutions may place all guidelines in one book. As institutions become larger and the organizations more complex, it becomes necessary to have a major handbook containing general policies for the entire institution, leaving departmental or program handbooks for the subdivision. Such books may contain only policies or a combination of policies and standard practices. If they contain a combination, they may be organized so that after each policy there will be found the standard practices that will implement it or so that the policies may be found in the first part of the book, with the standard practices following in the last part.

Those who have used loose-leaf notebooks have found that they permit changes to be made with the test confusion. Alphabetized index tabs with the subject indicated will assist in the organization of the handbook.

SAMPLE POLICIES AND STANDARD PRACTICES

As illustrations of how policies and standard practices might be written for an administrative handbook, four hypothetical examples are presented.

Policy I-Public Relations

All staff members have a responsibility for good public relations. Educational programs to be successful need the support of the many public. A sound program is the basis upto which good public relations rest.

Standard Practices

- Students who feel they are receiving something worthwhile and who are treated with the dignity that should be accorded all individuals are the most effective public relations agents. Teachers and coaches should avail themselves of opportunities to assist in this effort.
- Teachers and coaches should watch for opportunities to interpret programs to the public. All should participate in affairs where parents and other members of the general public are present. Within appropriate limits, opportunities to speak at civic functions should be accepted.
- Good human relations result in good public relations, Sincerity, integrity, and friendliness will pay dividends in acceptance by the public.

Policy II-Purchasing Equipment

The director of the division of physical education and athletics is ultimately responsible for the purchasing of physical education and athletic equipment. However, each staff member has a role. Every teacher and coach must assist in the assessment of needs and recommendations for the best and most appropriate equipment. All staff members must follow the specific procedures outlined in the standard practices when initiating purchases.

Standard Practices

- Each staff member responsible for initiating a purchase must investigate the costs, possible sources, and quantities needed. A check on the inventory should be made when necessary.
- All purchase must be initiated on the standard requisition form, which should be completed in every detail. The signature of the initiator should be affixed in the appropriate place.
- Requisitions must be approved and signed by the director of the division and will then be forwarded to the central purchasing office, where the purchase order will be completed.
- The initiator is responsible for examing the equipment when received and also for indicating approval for payment on the appropriate form. This should be sent to the director's office, which will then forward it to the controller for payment.

Policy III-Employment of Personnel

The basic principle for guiding the employment of personnel will be "the best person for the job." This implies a careful analysis of the education, experience, and personal qualifications of the candidates.

- Unless it is obviously impossible or inappropriate, a committee of staff members intimately concerned will be appointed as a "search committee" to seek candidates from many sources and to review the problems carefully.

- The search committee will present in writing to the director two or three names ranked in order of preference. These individuals will normally be brought in for personal interviews.
- The director will confer with the academic dean or principal regarding the committee's recommendations. The final selection will then be made.
- Qualification considered especially important are integrity, teaching competence, diligence, sincerity, commitment to the students' welfare, interest in people, intelligence, tact, and friendliness. These should be assessed to the extent possible.

Policy IV—Affirmative Action

The basic purpose of the affirmative action plan is to ensure that all personnel are treated fairly. There will be no discrimination on the basis of creed, race, ethnic background, or gender. All individuals will be given equal opportunities to succeed and advance to the degree that their performance, qualifications, and worth to the institution merit.

Standard Practices

- When employing personnel, the announcements of vacancies will be distributed so they will reach all individuals who may be qualified and interested.
- There will be no discrimination against minority groups when administering the programs of promotions, salary increments, and advancement.
- When employing new personnel, there should be an effort to strike a reasonable balance between persons of the various races, creeds, ethnic groups, and sexes.

- There will be compensatory and tutorial programs established to help disadvantaged students meet admission requirements.

These are partial examples of how policies and standard practices might be developed and placed in an administrative handbook. Each topic should begin on a new page so a single policy can be replace without disturbing others.

SUGGESTED SUBJECTS FOR POLICIES AND STANDARD PRACTICES

Policies and standard practices that might be included in departments of physical education and athletics are listed under the following headlines:

PERSONNEL POLICIES

- Tenure and dismissal
- Contracts
- Sick leave
- Leave of absence
- Classification and promotion
- Salary schedules and policies
- Retirement
- Credit unions
- Vacations
- Work load
- Teacher evaluation
- Affirmative action
- Collective bargaining

STAFF WORK

- Importance of complete fact-finding
- Written reports
- Appropriate coordination

CLASS ORGANIZATION AND CONDUCT

- Attire
- Attendance and make-up
- Record books
- Use of student leaders
- Grading and evaluating
- Changing class sections

HEALTH SERVICE

- Reporting of accidents, injuries, and sickness
- School nurse
- School physician
- Injury care
- Student health

FACILITIES

- For classes
- For curricular activities
- Outside group usage
- For free play (not class or curricular)
- Priorities, assignment, etc.

TEACHERS' OR COACHES' ABSENCES

- Reporting
- Sickness
- Trips
- Substitute teachers
- Other arrangements

ATHLETICS

- Scheduling
- Athletic trips
- Eligibility
- Insurance
- Personal car
- Training rules
- Playing on outside teams
- Parking during contests
- Recruiting
- Fund raising
- Safety of athletes

EQUIPMENT

- Purchase
- Care
- Custody
- Checking out and in
- Responsibility and accountability

KEYS

- Responsibility
- Accountability

IN-SERVICE EDUCATION

- Travel to conferences, etc.
- Advanced study
- Professional leaves
- Remuneration

DEPARTMENTAL MEETINGS

- Attendance
- Agenda
- Participation

REPORTS

- Special (injuries, unusual events)
- Trips and convention
- Annual
- Seasonal

COMMITTEE WORK

- Assignments
- Reporting
- Service limit

FINANCIAL ADMINISTRATION

- Budgeting
- Financial aid

- Accounting

PROFESSIONAL ETHICS COMMUNICATION

- Interdepartmental
- Extradepartmental
- Channels

OUTSIDE RELATIONSHIPS

- Municipal government
- Civic organizations
- Grants
- General public

SUPERVISION

- Philosophy
- Responsibility
- Student-teacher relationships

FORMULATING AND ESTABLISHING POLICIES AND STANDARD PRACTICES

- The philosophy, policies, and edicts of the institution should be carefully studies. All departmental guidelines should be compatible with those of the institution.
- State and local laws, municipal regulations, and any other pertinent rules and practices should be reviewed for their relevance to new policies.
- Departmental staff members should be involved on the basis of their special responsibilities their ability to write or edit, their role in implementation, and their interest in the project.

- An overall editorial committee should be formed and changed with the responsibility for uniformity of format, clarity of statements, and good writing.
- Subcommittees should be appointed for each area or topic for which guidelines are being written.
- Individuals with some executive responsibilities should be involved in the formulation of policies; persons at the operating level should have most to say about standard practices.
- When policies have been formulated by individual committees, they shall be presented to the department for discussion and approval. Revisions can be made at that time.
- The department director should present new policies to superiors for their approval. When approved by the institution, they become effective.
- Policies should be flexible enough to allow some leeway for those who implement them. They shall be reviewed periodically for needed changes.

SUMMARY

The role of planning is to take action in the present that will serve as a guide for the future. Administrators outline the steps that advance the organization toward its goals.

Thorough planning tends to lessen the number of random action, to avoid role conflict, to reduce dissatisfaction, and to diminish the number of arbitrary promotions and dismissals. It also leads to more consistent review of current actions and to meticulous care of important records.

The planning process includes the development of objectives, policies, standard practices, and programs. In a school system, the entire operation is dependent on the enrolment and the resources. These must be assessed before the program can be set in motion.

Policies are guiding principles that have been approved by a supervisory or legislative body for the operation of a department or other unit of a school or college. Executive functions include responsibility for the implementation of policies. This usually results in the promulgation of more specific policies or standard practices at the operational level.

Policies will be implemented more willingly if those who are responsible for implementing them have a voice in the formulation of the policies. Administrators at each level of the hierarchical organization should provide for the necessary representation.

Clearly articulated policies and carefully spelled-out standard will prevent misunderstandings and lead to more efficient and effective operation. They are also very important as criteria upon which evaluation and controlling can be based.

13

NEW DIRECTIONS IN SPORTS AS A FIELD OF STUDY

Until the 1960s the dominant steam of research in sporting areas was in physical education or in practical matters related to sporting practices. During the 1960s a new direction appeared in physical education: a growing scholarly interest in the study of sport. The result has been a startling change in research directions and concentration during the last decade and a half. This chapter will look at the rise of the disciplines in the field of physical education, along with the idea of sport as a legitimate field of scholarly study, and then briefly discuss some of the new fields of study in sport.

THE EMERGENCE OF A DISCIPLINE IN PHYSICAL EDUCATION

We have already discussed the emergence of the discipline side of physical education in the first chapter, but a short review will help in understanding developments in sports study in the 1970s. We defined a discipline as "an area of knowledge and theory that can exist purely for itself" that is, with no need to show that it has a practical application. The interest in this side of physical education began to develop in the mid-1960s.

The interest in a discipline centred around Henry's 1964 article and its implications. While various scholars, such as Kenyon, worked to define a discipline and its area of study, AAPER worked to organize and present a document which would demonstrate physical education's body of knowledge." At the same time, scholars in the Big Ten Conference schools organized a series of annual conference to discuss the different newly emerging disciplines or subdisciplines in what some scholars were beginning to call "sport studies." By the early 1970s publication had appeared from AAHPER which attempted to organize the theoretical base underlying physical education. Meanwhile, the American Academy of Physical Education debated whether a new name was needed for physical education, one which would better demonstrate the true focus of its study.

In this year since Henry's article first appeared and spurred interest in a discipline many changes in direction have affected-and are continuing to affect-physical education. The first notable change has been the split in physical education between the professional interests and the disciplinary interest. Many conflicts have arisen which seem to pit physical education against sport studies and "teachers" against "researchers." The more practical appearance of the profession side of studies has created problems with those interested in the discipline or research side, as each sometimes question the other's validity or importance.

In truth, both groups contribute to physical education in important ways. Their conflicts often seem to be little more than arguments of different points of view, though sometimes the real argument has bee over which group wields the power in a department. However, the scholarly side of physical education is far more prominently displayed today than it has been in the past.

A second notable change has been the appearance of new professional societies representing the disciplinary subgroups and their particular scholarly focus of interests. These new societies, which represent areas such as sport philosophy, sport sociological, sport history and sport psychology, have promoted scholarship in their areas by initiating national conferences and by publishing journals that provide more scholarly and wide-raging outlets of research than provided by the older organizations of physical education. By the mid-1970s AAHPERD and recognized the growth of the scholarly interests and had stared "Academies" within its professional structure.

A third notable change in the direction of physical education has been evident in the last decade or so. These years have seen a great burst of scholarly research and writing. Books of readings in scholarly areas have reflected this growth by their need of extensive revising as the quality and quantity of research continues to radically increase. This growth of scholarship has perhaps done the most in terms of reviving physical education and in presenting it to the outside world as an academically respectable field of study and work.

SPORT—A LEGITIMATE FIELD OF ACADEMIC STUDY

Sport holds a prominent place in modern life. Millions of people participate in sporting activities, watch and read about them, and spend billions of dollars annually on sports-related activities and equipment. Though this massive interest in sport was noticed many decades ago, little attention was paid to actually studying except by sport journalists and by the occasional scholar, whose professional co-workers often considered the pursuit of such interests as scholarly "slumming." Indeed, scholarly suspicion of the idea of a "scholarly" interest in sport still exists. But the impact of sport on modern society has made it clear that sport is a very legitimate field of academic study. As Max Scheler noted over half a century ago, "Scarcely an international phenomenon of the day deserves social and psychological study to the degree that sport does. Sport has gown immeasurably in scope and in social importance, but the meaning of sport has received little in the way of serious attention."

We now see sport used at the international level for many blatantly political purposes; prestige, a show of friendship, a show of international acceptance, and so forth. China invited the United States to send a table-tennis team on a tour as a sign of improving relations between the countries. Cuba used the 1976 Olympic victories of Alberto Junatorena as an argument for the superiority of their political system in improving life in their nation. Just as Hitler used the 1936 Olympics to show the "superiority" of his Nazi system, so did the Soviet union use the 1980 Olympics to serve the same flagrant propaganda purposes for their communist system. The Soviets published many articles stating that the awarding of the games to Moscow showed that the world had accepted the legitimacy of their communist government and, indeed, had approved of Moscow's approach to world peace, which included sending an army into an adjoining nation prior to the games. The obvious political nature of sport was made more clear when the games.

The obvious political nature of sport was made clear when the United States and many other nations withdrew from those games, using their absence as a protest of the Soviet Union's political actions more than as a political perversion of the purpose of the Olympics. Indeed, just as in 1936, the International Olympic Committee showed no sign of protest at the use of the game for political means by the host nation.

Sometimes we fail to realize the extent of our interest in sport in modern times. As Guttmann notes:

One reason that sports are not understood is that familiarity has made their significance seem obvious when its is not. Another reason is that the philosophers, historians, sociologists, and psychologist who have concerned themselves with sports have only rarely written for the ordinary reader. They have communicated mainly with each other.

Over the last decade and a half we have seen the rise of "sport science," the discipline arm of physical education. Though arguments for human movement as the focus of the discipline were advanced, more popularity seems to have settled on sport as the focus. Human movement has been called too broad, as it can include things such as learning to hold a pencil or to walk, while sport is more specific to the types of activities which are actually used in the field.

THE DISCIPLINES IN PHYSICAL EDUCATION

The fields of study or subdisciplines of sport are shown in the figure. Similar groupings have been suggested by other scholars, though Siedentop is one of the few who has called for the inclusion of pedagogy in the disciplines. The figure attempts to show the show the generally accepted subdisciplines within sport science and, at the same time, to show something of their relationships to each other. Sport pedagogy is concerned with teaching, particularly the skills used in sporting situations. It includes teaching methods and many elements tied to the concern of the profession of physical education. As the profession and professional preparation are discussed later, they will not be discussed further at this point. Discussions of the other six components follow.

Sport Biomechanics. Sport biomechanics is concerned with the effects of natural law and forces on the body in sport. It has developed from the field of kinesiology, which is also a study of movement. Kinesiology has two basic areas: anatomical kinesiology, which is concerned with the construction and working mechanisms of the body, and mechanical kinesiology, which is biomechanics or the mechanics of the human body. In sum, sport biomechanics is the study of the human body how the laws of physics apply to it.

Research in biomechanics breaks down into two large categories: fundamental study of the process of simple movements, and analysis of motor skills, which are far more complex and pertinent to sport skills. J. Ann Carr discusses seven types of research found in biomechanics. They are cinematography, stroboscope, force platform studies, electrogonimetry, electromyography, telemetry, and computer-based studies.

Cinematography uses motion picture photography to study movement. High-speed individual pictures are taken of many parts of a single continuing motion. Stroboscopy employs a similar photographic technique, except that an entire skill is captured in a single picture. A stroboscopic light flashes at preselected intervals of time during the performance. Only the positions at preselected intervals of time during the performance. Only the positions of the body photographed during the light flashes will show up on the picture, thus providing a representative view of the entire pattern of motion.

A force platform measures the force pushing against it, such as the amount of push a jumper uses in leaving the ground. It is used in studying the size and direction of forces, as well as their duration, and helps give a clearer idea of the variables in performances of skills such as the sprint start.

Electrogoniometry records changes in joint angles with electrical instruments, giving a clearer idea of the sequence and ranges of motion followed in performing a skill. Electromyography uses electrical instruments to record the work of muscles during the performance of skills. It can tell what muscles are used in performing a complex skill. Telemetry uses electrical instruments to record electrical "events" in the body, which means any physical activity that can be converted into an electrical signal such as a heartbeat. Small radio transmitters are then used to send the signal to recording instrument so that the performer can be studied while actually taking part in a normal performance, such as recording the activity of the heart of someone competing in a one-mile race.

Computers are being increasingly used to help analyse complied skill performance. In fact, they can now be used to simulate skill activities. The mechanical characteristics of a performer, such as a discus thrower, can be fed into a computer and displayed on a screen, along with information on the thrower's performance. The computer then can simulate or predict how far the discus would have been thrown if certain improvements in the thrower's technique had been made. This gives the performer a clearer idea of how a skill be improved and the potential gain which might come from this improvement.

The motion analyses of biomechanics look at two aspects of motion study: kinematics and kinetics. Kinematics seeks information on the motion of the body, regardless of what causes the motion. Kinetics studies what causes the body to move the way it does. There are many other subdivisions of areas within biomechanics, such as mechanics and dynamics, and even lower subdivisions, such as fluid mechanics, but these are better discussed in a biomechanics course. Kinetics and kinematics themselves are subdivision of dynamics, which is simply the study of motion.

Many groups are concerned with sport biomechanics, and numerous meetings are held at the national and international level to discuss research in the field. In addition, many biomechanical studies are published each year in the Research Quarterly for Exercise and Sport, a publication of AAHPERD. Within AAHPERD there is a discipline-oriented academy in kinesiology, which is devoted to encouraging scholarship in this area.

The future of biomechanics should include more joint research projects with either motor-learning specialists interested in determining how skills are learned and what are the most efficient teaching procedures, or with coaches interested in improving the technical performances of athletes through utilization of the scientific expertise and research capabilities of modern programs. The sport-and-athletics-oriented use of biomechanics is already a conspicuous part of Eastern European athletics, with East Germany and the Soviet Union leading the way in the application of research capabilities to athletic performance.

SPORT PHYSIOLOGY

Sport physiology is concerned with how the body functions during exercise. The effects of training are a critical facet of sport physiology research, which makes it perhaps the most important of the sport studies, for it is concerned with all aspects of how the body adapts to exercise. This includes such concerns as the function and contraction of the muscles, the workings of the nervous system during physical activity, the functions of the respiratory system, and the working of the cardiovascular system.

At the same time, this area of study if often considered to include sport medicine, an equally important and growing area of study. Sport medicine is concerned with both treating and preventing athletic injuries. In turn, this broad interest in the health or the physically active body also can include adapted physical education, or developmental activities for the physically of mentally handicapped or disabled. The sports medicine specialist is concerned with preventive training, treatment, and equipment that assist the performer in staying healthy; nutrition; drugs and erogogenic aids; the treatment and rehabilitation of injuries; and ethical matters related to the training, exercise, and treatment of athletes.

The sport physiologist conducts research studies in a physiology laboratory, using such equipment as treadmills, exercise bicycles, oxygen measuring equipment, and equipment that measures chemical characteristics of the body. Where the sport biomechanics specialist works in areas of physics, the sport physiologist works basically in areas related to chemistry. More or the work of the sport physiologist takes place in the laboratory than of the sport biomechanics specialist. Yet, the importance of the research of the physiologist is great, for the work cuts to the heart of the training system; unless an athlete is trained to a fine edge and to the highest level, good mechanics will not result in high-level performances.

Groups interested in the study of sport physiology include the Exercise physiology. Academy of AAHPERD, which encourages scholarly study among the professional membership; the American College of Sports Medicine, which encourages and publishes research in that area; and the National Athletic Trainer's Association, which encourages study in that area. The American Medical Association has a Committee on the Medical Aspects of Sports that actively works with physicians and keeps them informed of matters relating to sports problems, injury, and treatment. The work of this committee ha become especially important due to the great in crease in participation in competitive sports and to the related rise in sports injuries, many of which are treated by doctors who normally do not work with sports injuries.

Publications in the field include the Research Quarterly for Exercise and Sport, published by AAHPERD; the periodical Medicine and Science in Sports, published by the ACSM; and the book the Encyclopedia of Sport Sciences and Medicine, also published by the ACSM. Many national and international conferences on the subject are help each year by different groups interested in sports physiology.

The future of sport physiology will probably include more coordinated studies with coaches that are designed to learn how to determine and properly monitor optimal training levels in exercise programs. These studies will utilize testing of the cardio-respiratory system and of blood chemistry. Much work in this area has already been done in East Germany and the Soviet union.

Currently, much research is being conducted by sport physiologists in the prevention of athletic injuries and in the development of better programs to prepare people for exercise programs and to help people recover swiftly from injuries. At the same time, work is also being done to prepare more athletic trainers and to educate more doctors in sports medicine so that prevention and treatment will be raised to a higher level in the United States.

In addition, work is being done by sport physiologists in areas related to the needs of the physically handicapped. This work includes the development of rehabilitation methods and programs and the development of more "normal" programs of physical education and sport for the handicapped. The impetus provided by federal regulations, such as PL 94-142, which require the "main streaming" of handicapped individuals into non-handicapped programs, has resulted in far more attention and money for this area than at any time in the past.

OTHER DISCIPLINES

Sport philosophy has been discussed at some length, so it will not be discussed within this chapter. The areas of sport psychology, sport sociology and sport history will be discussed within the context of the social sciences.

STUDYING SPORT IN THE SOCIAL SCIENCES

Physical education and sporty studies have been traditionally associated with scientific studies, but in recent years increasing attention has been paid to the potential of sport research in the social sciences. We can simplify the distinction between the sciences and the social sciences by looking at the sciences as concerned basically with physical phenomena, while the social sciences are concerned with social phenomena. The most commonly understood social sciences in sport studies are psychology, sociology, and history. We will briefly discuss each of these social sciences in order to give a fuller idea of the focus and method of each in sport studies.

SPORT PSYCHOLOGY

Sport psychology is concerned with studying human behaviour in the sport setting. In the realm of sport studies, psychology is often studied in two aspects: motor sill learning and performance, which is common to both physical education and sport and to sport is concerned with the psychological factors affecting the learning and performance of physical skills—with how individuals are affected by both internal and external factors.

Among the earliest works in sport psychology were two books by Coleman R. Griffith, Psychology of Coaching and Psychology and Athletics. Clearance Ragsdle published an dearly work, The psychology of Motor Learning, and John Lawther published The Psychology of Coaching in 1951. Even so , sport psychology was a relatively new territory when large-scale interest began to develop in the 1960s.

The International Society of sports Psychology was organized at the First International Congress of Psychology of Sport in Rome in 1965, while the North American Society for the Psychology of Sport and Physical activity was founded in 1966. When the idea of discipline-centred academies to promote scholarship appeared in the early 1970s, the Sport Psychology Academy was begun in 1975, with the somewhat related Motor Development Academy following in 1979. Both within the professional arm of physical education, AAHPERD.

While articles relating to sport psychology may be found frequently in the Research Quarterly for Exercise and Sport and occasionally in Quest, the primary scholarly publications are the *International Journal of Psychology of Sport*, the *Journal of Sport Psychology the Journal of Motor Behaviour*, and *Perceptual and Motor Skills*.

Sports psychology studies such issues as the nature of motor skill, performance and learning ,and the psychological characteristics of the performer. The factors that are studied include those affecting physical performance such as motivation, the distribution of practice, and the specificity. The difference in these factors in the teaching situation and the coaching situation is primarily one of the level of skill and intensity of the performer, as the basic factors and principles are the same.

Some sport psychologists are debating the direction to be taken in sport psychology research, particularly in methodology. Rainer Martens has called for more emphasis on "field" research—that is, research which studies performance where it takes place, on the track or playing field, rather than traditional laboratory research. In the past most research has been with individuals or groups in a laboratory setting which is a carefully monitored environment. Martens notes the existence of the question of why sport psychologists spend so little time actually studying sport, or applied research. In response, he suggests that more theory-building work is necessary and that doing it will require more time studying sport where and as it takes place.

Martens does note that research can be just as erroneous as any other type of research, but says that laboratory research often is not useful in the field situation. The essential problem is the complexity of human behaviour. So many factors can affect a single situation that it may be impossible to determine how to change the factors if we want to increase or decrease some element of performance.

Siedentop agrees with Marten's suggestions that the field would be the best place for research in psychology and with the idea that new theories would be more likely to develop from field research which is concerned with applied problems. However, Siedentop does not agree with all of Marten's ideas. He notes that "sport psychology will become more accepted in the 'field' if it adopt a more client-centred approach. Sport psychologists are beginning to react to this call for more applied research into the actual sporting practice instead of lab experiments that often bear little fruit in the in the field.

Sport psychology is a field that is receiving growing interest. To date, psychologists in the Western world have only moderately active in working with athletes and teams, but in the Eastern socialist countries sport psychology has been increasingly present in the preparation of high-level athletes. This is the direction of the future. Coaches, teachers, and parents are becoming more concerned not only about preparing athletes for highly skilled performance, but also about protecting the emotional-psychological health of athletes.

Much work remains to be done by sport psychologists in terms of field and laboratory research; actual work coaches, athletes, and teams; the monitoring of programs, such as youth sports.

SPORT SOCIOLOGY

Sport sociology is concerned with the social behaviour of people in the sport setting, both individual and group behaviour. This broad area is sometimes described as studying the sociocultural processes and institutions as they relate to and are affected by sport and sport in behaviour. Sport is a significant part of our social order; it is often described as a "microcosm of society," that is, a small-scale model of what the whole society is like. The sport sociologist, studies how people interact with each other in a sport setting in order to determine how the process of sport affects their development and socialization, or how they fit into society.

Two aspects of society are studied by sport sociologists: social institutions, such as schools or other organizations, and social processes, such as the development of social status or prestige within a group or community. Social aspects of life are difficult to research, for they provide little truly objective data. Group and individual behaviour are studied by using sources such as interviews, official statistics, questionnaires, documents, observation, and experimentation. Such sources are rarely objective, however, since they require the opinion of an individual or group to group to determine a status or change.

As a result, sociological research results often are considered controversial. At the same time, the important part played by sport in the schools and in the community as children grow up requires that we learn as much as we can about how sport affects the social aspects of the growing process. Only with such knowledge in hand can sport be used in the most beneficial way in helping children grow into healthy, socially useful adults.

Areas of research in sport sociology include sport and social institutions social stratification, and socialization. Among the many sub-topics that are studied in relation to individuals and groups in sport are sexual differences and roles, racism, religion, values and ethics, economics, politics, leisure and work habits, ethnic groups, and social change.

Sport sociology is still a newer area of sport research, though a few of its scholarly works go back to the early years of this century such as Steinitzer's Sport and Culture, Rise's Sociology of Sport, Huizinga's Homo Ludens, and Caillois's Man, play, and games. Early suggestions for sport sociology as a subdiscipline in the United States were made by Gerald Kenyon and John Loy in 1965, and more specific explanations of the subject by Loy followed in 1968. Indeed, sport sociology was one of the first of the sporting disciplines or subdisciplines to develop its own scholarly organizations and publications apart from the usual small groups of physical educations that operate strictly within larger general conventions.

The Committee for the Sociology of Sport was an early branch of the International Council of Sport and Physical Education, and it was followed by the International Committee of Sport Sociology, which was founded in 1964. The ICSS has regular international sport sociology seminars and sponsors the International Review of Sport Sociology. The ICSS was followed by the North American Society for the Sport and by the Sport Sociology Academy, which was formed in the NASPE area of AAHPERD. Other sport sociology publications include the Sport Sociology Bulletin and the Journal of sport and Social Issues. Some sport history meetings and periodicals publish studies that can be termed sport sociology since areas of sociology may be studied in their historical context, such as whether sports participation was widely used in blending early immigrant groups into the existing communities in the United States.

SPORT HISTORY

Sport history is the study of sport in the past. It can serve to teach us how things have come to be as they are today, and it can direct us to problems that need to be solved. There are two today, and it can direct us to problems that need to be solved. There are types of historical research descriptive and interpretive. Descriptive historical research is the early groundwork for study, for it simply determines the facts of the matter—the "what" of history—and reports them. Early historical works are usually descriptive.

The more advanced level of historical research is interpretive: the attempt to tell or determine why something happened or what is important about an event or trend. Evidence must be not only analysed but also interpreted; this injects the issue of values and value systems into the research.

Sources for historical research are generally called primary of secondary sources. A primary source is any person or thing that was a direct witness to the event being studied. It may be the account of a person who was there, or it may be official record kept during the event. In short, the primary source is first-hand information. The secondary source is any source not directly involved in the event when it happened, such as the report of a person who interviewed someone who was a participant.

Historical research involves three basic concepts; change, development, and progress. Change is a simple concept—a difference from an earlier state or condition. Change can be documented easily because no values are involved. Either a rule did or did not change; the evidence is usually clear. Development is a series of changes in a direction; it, too is not difficult to establish with evidence. The speed of change in a direction can range from slow to fast and if it is consistent in a single direction, it can be documented to show a trend. Again, no values are involved. Simple facts can establish direction.

The third concept of historical research is progress, which does require value judgments and is thus less grounded in facts. Change and development are descriptive ideas, but progress is always interpretive because it assumes improvement. One of the difficulties of historical research is that many ideas are based on the concept of progress, which Robert Nisbet says has been an accepted concept for three thousand years of western history. Yet, the validity of progress as a concept is beginning to be questioned because it is so value-laden. As Nisbet summarizes it, "The idea of progress holds that man kind has advanced in the past—from some aboriginal condition of primitiveness, barbarism, or even nullity—is now advancing, and will continue to advance through the foreseeable future."

This idea, clearly is a value judgment, for one must believe in the idea of progress to begin with. The concept is critical to sport, since modern sport is very concerned with records and their breaking; only the belief in the idea of progress makes those records worth keeping, for they are goals to be surpassed, which is possible only if there is a belief in progress.

One of the early history books was Joseph Strutt's sports and Pastimes of the People of England. John A. Krout's annals of American Sport was the first scholarly book on sport history in the United States, though earlier writings on the subjects are available. Many of the sources on sport history are cited in a booklet produced in 1980 by the History of Sport and Physical Education Academy of the AAHPERD, Getting Started in the History of Sport and Physical Education. Excellent works on research methods also are available, such as the one by Jacques Barzun and Henry F. Graaf, while other works serve as an introduction to the problems of sport history research itself, such as the one by Allen Guttmann.

Sport history, with its concern about the when, where and how of sport, serves to complete the circle of studies covered in sport science. Obviously, not all of the components are sciences; for those areas of study not strictly considered science, the term "sport arts and sciences" for those areas of study not strictly considered science, the term " sport arts and sciences" has been suggested as has the term "sport social sciences." Sport history serves to show us where we have been, how we got where we are today, and, with a little luck, perhaps where we may be going and what we should look for.

A SUMMATION

We now have looked briefly at each of the disciplines or subdisciplines generally accepted as part of the field of sport science or sport studies. Scholars accept either six or seven areas as separate: sport biomechanics, sport physiology, sport philosophy, sport psychology, sport sociology, sport history, and sport pedagogy.

14

CONTRIBUTION AND RELATIONSHIPS OF HEALTH, PHYSICAL EDUCATION AND RECREATION TO FITNESS

The name, American Association for Health, Physical Education and Recreation, involves a number of varied, intricate and sometimes vague relationships. To the title physical education in our association's name, the world health was added, but no one stopped to ask what it included. An individual possesses health; associations are concerned with health education. More recently, the word recreation was added; and here again definitions became varied, ranging from concepts of sports and games to a wide gamut of creative activities, or to some it means recreation education.

We are involved in the meaning of terms and confusion reigns. A word means one thing to one and another to his neighbour, another to his professional associate, and still another to an administrator or to the public. This paper is an attempt to clarify this situation. As we move through the discussion, words and phrases will be defined and relationships established, from the viewpoint of the speaker.

PHASES OF DEVELOPMENT

Man may be thought of in terms of four phases of development: organic; neuromuscular; interpretive; and emotional. It is evident that all developments are bound into an integrated whole but the word fitness should be reserved for a quality of organic power. Yet, when fitness is discussed someone inevitably raises the question, "What about mental fitness? Does it involve native intelligence, the I.Q., educational advancement, emotional balance, or just what is it? Then someone raises the question of moral and spiritual fitness. Unfortunately, there is no clear cut meaning for these words, though apparently many people have. Is there a standard definition for these terms which has eluded me or are they qualities differing for each man?

The word fitness should be reserved for organic development optimum health. "Fit as a fiddle" is understood. When an athlete is "in the pink", we know what this means.

Total fitness is too vague a term. Such broad terms as "total" or "well-rounded" can be applied to all education, to life itself; but as the whole is the sum of its parts, can we not discuss the relationship of parts? If so, we must isolate physical fitness as the primary objective of physical education.

The physical education, health and recreation aspects of our education have been criticized for attempting to be all things to all men. Physical education and its associated areas cannot be all things to all men, but there are some things which they must be to all men.

Total fitness is the responsibility of all society-home, church, school and community. It seems to me that physical education should concern itself largely with the physical organism-optimum health. There will occur voices to defend fringe contributions of physical education and it should be agreed, but in the breakdown of responsibilities, our major task is the development of an organism capable of performing sustained effort.

Various phases of education are assigned specific points of emphasis. One stresses history and literature; another, the sciences; another languages; another citizenship and still another the arts of vocational training. All are, or should be, interested in the health and physical fitness of an individual and, likewise, physical education should be interested in and contribute to all educational objectives. The physical educator's primary responsibility, however, should remain focuses. One group of educators can select only a small portion of the total problem.

It would be better to talk about a man skilled in a specific activity rather than skill-fitness; the thinking, problem solving man rather than mental-fitness; the man who lives on an emotionally high level rather than moral-fitness. Health is only one phase of total man, and our responsibilities must be confined to this one phase though we, like every other discipline, contribute to the whole.

Men, throughout the ages, have been high on one or two of the four phases of development but seldom high on all four. Let us consider some examples. Gandhi was low on the organic level to the point of frailty. He wanted to weave but said, "My finger are all thumbs." Intellectually, he was fairly high though he failed as a lawyer. Emotionally, however, he was a mountain peak. He helped to free 150 million untouchables in India; he preached tolerance for which his enemies took his life.

In a like manner, mountain climbers and athletes while high on the organic and neuromuscular level may be at the same time either very low or very high on the intellectual and emotional levels. Examples of uneven development multiply with the names of Robert Louis Stevenson, Roosevelt and Elizabeth Barrett Browning all of who were frail but maintained peaks of achievement on other levels. There are, on the other hand, classic examples of people high on all levels, such as Robert Frost, Carl Sandburg, Winston Churchill, Jean Sibelius and Justice William O. Douglas. One could also cite many who are low on all the four levels of development. It is obvious that one can be skilful and intellectual yet not be high in other phases of development.

It is obvious too that one can be high or low in all. The point is that superiority in one phase of development does not guarantee the same pre-eminence in another.

ORGANIC DEVELOPMENT

This is the ability of the human organism to resist fatigue and to sustain effort. We need people, for war and peace, high on this level. With the high standard set by the armed forces, rejections will never be much lower than in World War-I1 because of hereditary backgrounds, accidents, or specific handicaps such as in eyes and ears and nerves.

We might think of health or physical fitness on a thermometer with the mercury moving up and down. Health is a condition of the organism. There are numerous factors which help to raise the mercury in this thermometer. Some are: protection from infections; good medical and dental advice and care; high hereditary background; good habits of nutrition, rest and sheep; adapted exercise; etc.

When the individual functions in an atmosphere of joy, happiness and challenge, he is training for fitness or optimum health-the mercury reading is high, but when he operates without these requisites, he causes the mercury on his health scale to lower. A high reading on this thermometer is to be desired.

Health or fitness, then, should be considered as a condition of the organism and not in terms of total life outcomes or objectives.

In a similar manner we might think of skills, the ability to think, and emotional status as thermometers with many elements tending to raise the mercury while others lower it. Illness and handicaps, hereditary or acquired, may readily lower or raise the skill-level or the thinking-level and may produce either bitterness or great faith. Elizabeth Barrett Browning when urged by her friends to stop working because of her ill health said, "If work means headaches, perforce it prefer headaches."

NEURO-MUSCULAR DEVELOPMENT

One may be highly or poorly skilled in any one of many areas-athletics, crafts, mechanics, science, painting, sculpturing, written or spoken language, picking pockets, or dozens more. The doers may be skilful and may be healthy but may not necessarily be ideal citizens. Skill ranges all the way from the beginning of gross movement to the performance of the artist. Skilful performance in strenuous activities helps the body to conserve energy and, hence, is closely related to organic development.

INTERPRETIVE DEVELOPMENT

This is the ability to think in one or more areas, to see relationships, to solve problems, to associate and remember, and to make sound judgements. A high rating on an intelligence test is not the sole criterion for this development. There are many kinds of intelligences, not just one. We think in terms of past experiences so we are largely a product of where we have been and what we have done. Skills give meaning to words and relationships. The hands are the "eye of the brain". Thinking in one area, however, seldom assures competency in another.

EMOTIONAL DEVELOPMENT

This involves the problem of attitudes and feelings. One the highest level, it may assume a religious concepts involving the mountain peaks of brotherhood and respect for all men. On the lower level it may be expressed in prejudice, hearted and intolerance.

These four developments are all related and the ideal is to be high on each of them but this attainment for all would be a utopia beyond the dream of the science fictionist.

DEFINITIONS

The next step is to discuss the meaning of several words which too often are taken for granted.

Physical education must be defined in terms of certain objectives. It can be illustrated, and desirable outcomes may be cited. It involves the total body: nerves, organs, muscles, the master brain and the emotions. Activities, other than physical education, are also dependent on these same physical sources. The farmer, the dock worker, and the bank president utilize similar body-brain-nerve and emotional connections, but physical education involves, activities whose primary outcome is in terms of organic and skill development. It is the training a man undergoes for the purpose of developing hid body, with all its related processes to function so that he may live to his fullest capacity.

Emotionally development is and should be a by-product of physical education. Exercise involved in games and sports, swimming and gymnastics, coming and outdoor education have specific objectives in terms of body power, endurance and behaviour. The objective here is exercise for health and organic development, while with the farmer, the carpenter and the dock worker the exercise involved in the pursuit of each and its outcomes is not the primary objective. The results in the finished product becomes the desired outcome.

Re-physical education has been used as a substitute for the term rehabilitation. Here again the object of the exercise is re-educating the body, not papering a board.

Recreation education, one of the primary responsibilities of teacher training, refers to the process of exposing young and old to satisfying recreational pursuits, of helping them skilfully in leisure and of providing good facilities for them.

Health is the ability to sustain effort and recover from fatigue quickly. It should be thought of, ideally, in terms of optimum organic functioning.

Health education on the other hand, involves a total educational process and is the result of the efforts of many people who try to raise the health status of man on the mercury scale.

RELATIONSHIPS

There are three relationships which must be considered: the relationship of health to physical education; the relationship of physical education to recreational; and the relationship of recreation to health.

HEALTH AND PHYSICAL EDUCATION

This is primarily a relationship of exercise to optimum health within the individual's capacity. If you prefer, call it fitness. Many facets which promote optimum health and longevity are outside the physical education domain. Optimum health is promoted by the doctor, dentist, nurse, sanitation and public health officials, nutritionists and others who provide a wholesome atmosphere in which a person lives.

Exercise contributes in at least five areas. When many variables affects the health of man it is always difficult to prove this-did-that or if-he-had-done-this, the-result-would-have-been-that. It is very difficult to draw always or never conclusions. Man must take the advice of experts for they, by training and experience, are in the best position to know the truth. The expert source from which the following was drawn is exercise and health, published by the American Medical Association.

A general conclusion of the relationships of the physical education type of exercise and health is provided in a joint statement made by the American Medical Association and the American Association for health, physical education, and Recreation:

1. Exercise is one of the most important factors contributing to total fitness.

2. The contributions of exercise to fitness include the development and maintenance of strength, speed, agility, endurance, and skill in persons who are physiologically sound. Active games, sports, swimming, rhythmic activities, prescribed exercises, and vigorous hobbies, such as gardening and other work around the home, all can make distinctive as well as worthwhile general contributions to fitness.

3. Individuals differ in their capacity to enjoy and benefit from participation in exercise because of constitutional variations in body size, strength, and structure as well as differences in previous experience and present condition.

4. Exercise should be graded according to age, individual reaction to activity, and the state of the person's fitness. After age 40, more frequent medical evaluation of the individual's capacity for exercise is imperative.

5. Activities for girls and women should be selected with regard for their psychological as well as physiological characteristics. Those which involves a minimum of body contact and do not stress heavy lifting should be favoured. Regularity of exercise should be stressed, with activity continued. If it is well tolerated, during the menstrual period.

6. The training involved in preparation for athletic competition contributes as much to fitness as participation in the contests themselves. Systematic training for any activity contributes effectively to fitness.

7. Time and care taken to condition the body for sports and athletics through appropriate activities will improve enjoyment, upgrade performance, and increase the ability to continue participation over a period of years.

8. Certain types of exercises are appropriate to certain conditions of weather and climate. Common sense suggests that a person should not set excessive performance goals under unfavourable conditions.

9. The proper use of protective equipment is essential to safe and effective participation in certain sports. Careful maintenance and proper control of facilities for athletics and other types of participation will help to prevent accidents and reduce injuries.

10. The rules of the game or specifications for play in an activity are made to protect participants and to enhance enjoyment. They should be properly interpreted, scrupulously observed, and vigorously enforced.

11. The vigour with which an individual participates in an activity will have more to do with outcomes for fitness than the activities or events in which he elects to participate.

PHYSICAL EDUCATION AND RECREATION

There is a vital relationship between physical education and certain phases of recreation but always keep in mind that recreation in a much broader term than is implied in sports and games. For activity to have any value there must be sustained effort. In order to sustain effort there must be drive, interest and fun. Recreation, therefore, which takes one camping and in the out-of-doors, which gives a person enjoyment in a game of tennis, badminton or swimming, form a real point of articulation with physical education.

Even at retirement, slowing up a little should not mean coming to a complete stop. Life has a quick way of disposing of non-workers and inactive persons. Retirement should never be the lazy man's dream of doing nothing. Explosive types of exercises or exercise too long sustained or engaged in at high altitudes should be avoided but other exercises should be carried on not just to the age of forty but to seventy-five and eighty-five. Recreation-fun is the catalyst which sets off desirable fitness outcomes.

RECREATION AND HEALTH

There is a physiological rule called the "law of attention"-namely, when the organism gives its attention to an activity (to grasp a fishing rod, or a golf club, or a lathe or a violin), worries and tensions disappear. The 20th century killers are fears, insecurities and tensions. We are living in a coronary-stomach ulcer-decade and excessive tensions are the cause relaxing recreation, hobbies in the best sense, is needed.

We need some tensions, of course, as in the uncertainty of the game, the thrill of a new struggle, the hope of success. Boredom has many of the characteristics of fatigue. The answer to many a health problem is to get into action, do something in which you are interested, find a hobby, get going! The other end of the scale from boredom is undue tension.

Man has a quality of oneness. Happiness, just old-fashioned joy, which means the absence of stress, supports buoyant health in a positive way and helps to keep the body resistance high. Happiness is associated with challenge, accomplishment and mastery. Happiness involves hope and faith.. Hope, faith and joy are medicinal. They are therapeutic. They represent the difference between living and existing and often, between life and death. Happiness, however, is more than entertainment and amusement, money or "eat, drink and be merry." The basic need is to have a goal in work and recreation, a feeling of being wanted, of belonging, of sacrificing for a worthwhile cause.

CHALLENGE

We now have ample support from scientists that health has a relationship to the religious, spiritual, work and recreational phases of life. One must see meaning in life. One must have a goal and travel hopefully to live and be healthy.

It is recognized that there are many other relationships between physical education and various life outcomes, following philosophical and physiological principles of living, but still the main objective of physical education remains organic development-health.

It must be apparent that desirable outcomes of education and of life and the outcomes of physical education cannot be adequately tested by any quantitative measurements. We can test speed, strength, agility, and to some extent, endurance, but we cannot test the will to live, the will to do and the will to conquer.

We have heard a great deal about the necessity of health and fitness, particularly since 1918; but so far as the schools are concerned, it has been mostly talk. As Russia increased the pressure of studies in the school-room, it correspondingly increased the time devoted to physical education. Rear Admiral H. G. Rickover commented wisely, "While you are developing the minds of children develop also their bodies through physical education. These, too, are paramount."

We still need today, however, some things to help people. In the modern school program we must have a longer day. This extended time should lay the basis for a health-fitness-exercise program; it should also give children some leisure time opportunities in the performing arts. We could have a longer school week. Most European schools carry on for six days. In this time our children could master one or two foreign languages, improve their English and arouse curiosity through science.

There could even be a longer school year. Summers could be utilized for work experience in factory, shop and farm, or in well organized private and school camps. Boys and girls could get experience in conservation, in preserving and replanting national and state forests and in working on public lands. These areas of educational could be as valuable as those in the class rooms.

For total development, education must recognize the many talents of young and old- the many phases of development: organic, neuromuscular, interpretive and emotional. There would be no drop-outs if the school curriculum were broad enough to meet the interests and abilities of all children. We need redirection of outcomes. Thus optimum health-fitness-citizenship and joy in living would be encouraged.

The boys and girls of this country deserve administrative backing from our state and local boards of education and from all school administrative officials. Our young people have the will and all life is reborn with every child. We must not falter now.

15

SIGNIFICANT EXPERIENCES—A CHALLENGE TO PHYSICAL EDUCATION

The word "significant" comes from two root words "signum," which means sign or mark, and "facere," to make, therefore an experience that makes a mark is a significant experience. Everybody wants to make a mark in the world. The kind of mark seems to vary with age. A boy wants to be a circus clown. Then he wants to be like his dad-that doesn't last very long! Then he wants to be a fireman, then he wants to make All State, then he wants to get rich; later on he wants to make both ends meet, and finally he hopes to get his old age pension. So really these marks vary.

Another way to think about this is to inquire what experiences are remembered. There is a school of psychology that places great emphasis on what you remember from your early childhood. A person stuck his neck out once to tell another person that he remembered a fight at age 5 with his brother in which each of them got hold of the same rocking chair and ended by pulling it apart. Of course, the fellow analysed it to show aggressiveness because the incident remembered was a fight. But since the recollection is that we came apart each with his share, like breaking up a wishbone, may be we were interested in sharing.

Every significant experience is in some way connected with strong feeling tone and this feeling tone makes it significant. Let us say the "heat" of the feeling burns the mark into our memory.

NEUROLOGY OF A SIGNIFICANT EXPERIENCE

In a model brain one sees the parts of the brain that react in what is called a significant experience. It would have taken more than this brain to answer this question in old testament days when, you remember, God searched the reins and the heart of man. The reins-that is the kidneys-were the seat of the mind and the heart the location of the sound. In New Testament times, we would have needed to bring along also the "bowels of tender mercy." Saint Paul speaks of the emotions being in the abdomen. But today we have it all localized up here in the head. Gall and Spurzheim in 1829 stood before the Society of Biology in Paris to enunciate the principles of phrenology. These gentlemen had left bumps on peoples' heads and were quite sure that by feeling around up there they could tell what was wrong or what was right with a person. Thus, they located the liberty axis up on top and to one side of it religion and the other side love. What could be nicer to encircle liberty. In high school my physiology teacher told us that bumps behind the ears meant that you were destructive. So all of us Lane Tech Indians felt behind our ears and found we were destructive.

The significant fact of phrenology is its attempt to connect parts of the brain with character traits-loyalty, honesty, purity, observing power, etc. This is the older viewpoint which now is found only where somebody sells rattlesnake oil with a picture of the brain as a backdrop.

Today we know the motor cortex, where stimulation causes movement in muscles of the other side. We know the sensory cortex where stimulation gives rise to sensations of touch in various parts of the body. Back of this is an area which is necessary for sight and just in front of it is one for the interpretation of sight. On the anterior missal surface there is something for smell and taste, and here on the temporal lobe is something for hearing. Other areas are less well understood.

This is fairly good evidence that memories are stored in the cortex, and that these memories can be brought out by electrical stimulation. They are also brought out by the stimulation accompanying epileptic attacks and account for the aura that precedes the attack. To know where to operate, the surgeon now stimulates until he finds a spot that produces an experience similar to the aura that regularly precedes an attack. Removal of this area often brings relief from epileptic seizures.

But that is only part of the story. Simultaneously with these advances regarding the cortex some astonishing discoveries were made in the basal part of the brain. It goes back to the 30's when professor Hess of Zurich found some 4,000 spots in the cat's brain stem which when stimulated gave rise to different actions in the cat, such as blinking, purring, falling asleep, and combinations of some activities. Here was uncovered a rudimentary brain that must have existed millions of years ago before this top cortex business arrived to make us human. This rudimentary brain still works in us.

Near the front end of the brain stem are centres for anger, rage, and pain, in the diencephalon. Just above these are pleasure centres. An electrode placed into this part of the brain can be wired so that when a cat touches a certain button it apparently feels a sensation of pleasure. Now this cat might, in the course of an hour, accidentally touch the button 15 to 20 times but when a circuit is connected so that it stimulates itself, it will do it 5000 times an hour to get this sensation of pleasure. So we know "pleasure" is located in the brain stem. We know pain is in there, too. We know other reactions of the body connected with the viscera are located here. This is the great new discovery-the reticular formation as it is called. We know that this part is connected with the cortex for two way communication. So every idea, if we could think of it that way, is connected with feelings down in this part and the feeling centres in turn communicate with the cortex. There is thus continuous interrelationship between ideas and the centres for feeling tone, and we begin to see what happen if we want feelings connected with experiences, so that when either is activated the other, also, reacts.

Then, also, there is a rather peculiar bump up front called the prefrontal lobe which is one of the most recent developments of the brain not found in the China man, at least not as far as we can reconstruct from his skull. Thus prefrontal lobe has a few interesting stories connected with it.

In 1848 Phineas Gage, a very sedate, Puritan-like man living in New England, while tamping gun powder into a blasting hole had the powder explode and drive the tamping rod into his prefrontal lobe. This has become the famous crowbar case of Harvard Medical School. This caused Phineas to change his nature completely. Previously a very honest, home-loving, well-disciplined, conscientious man, now with the piece of metal in his prefrontal lobe he was an entirely different person-no more a good Puritan as you would picture such a person. He lost interest in his family and became in a sense a loose liver.

Sometime later a woman became much depressed. So she put a gun to the side of her head and shot. She didn't die. When the haemorrhage cleared out or her eyes she recovered to appear rather normal. Instead of being completely depressed, she was now outgoing. She had shot off her worry bump.

It is not evident whether she was depuritanized as was good old Phineas, but there have been many operations like that since. It is called *psycho-surgery*. The prefrontal lobe of the brain is in a very special way connected with the diencephalon where nerve centres controlling emotional tone are lodged. Too much connection with these centres results in overloading our experiences with affective states, sometimes resulting in withdrawal. Consequently, an operation to sever this connection may bring relief. This was first done on may be Portuguese neurologist, Moniz, in 1936.

Through the prefrontal lobes there are nerve paths that connect the cortex where ideas are stored with the centres of feeling. Incidentally, removal of the prefrontal lobes doesn't change your IQ by the ordinary tests; but you are not as wise as you were before. Knowing facts and being able to answer an examination is knowledge. Wisdom is knowing how to use these facts and this is in some way connected with feeling. When you begin to connect feelings with ideas then you may sense that one is better than other. When you connect pain with one kind of action and pleasure with another, you have the beginning of conscience. Dr. Dandy, one of the early surgeons on this part of the brain, had removed the prefrontal lobe from a patient whom he retained at the hospital as a handyman. One day Dr. Dandy assigned this handyman without a prefrontal lobe to show some noted visiting neuro-surgeons around the hospital grounds before bringing them to his office. These surgeons noted nothing unusual in the handyman.

People who lack prefrontal lobes often do a lot of bragging and punning, but who doesn't sometimes! May be they just lack structurally what some of us lack functionally. Thus far we have seen that in man's brain they are opportunities for all connections necessary to make a significant experience, i.e., to tie ideas up with feeling tone and to inject feeling tone back into the ideas. This is the neurological basis of significant experiences.

SIGNIFICANT EXPERIENCE AND AGE LEVELS

Let us go beyond neurology to think in terms of significant experiences at various ages in life, particularly those experiences about which physical education can do something and which therefore are a challenge to physical education. Let us think of the child that is just beginning to crawl in its crib. It raises its head and moves around, it pulls up one arm and finally it stands up very proudly. Of course it doesn't say, "I'm proud"; but look at it and you can tell that it feels proud of what it can do.

Then pretty soon it starts to climb. A little later it climbs up and jumps down. Then it climbs a little higher and a little higher before jumping. Imagine what is happening in the brain of this child. We know that the cortex is very poorly developed. The child cannot write a letter to its Senator, it cannot debate with its parents. All it can do, at least all that can be mentioned in public, is jump, struggle, spit, and cry. These are all muscular activities. Now imagine that this child has climbed up on a rock. Now look at it. The child is excited, leaning forward. You can see expressions of pleasure, of excitement, and a little fear all in that same face. Here it faces a challenge. It calls, "Mama, look." No! No! No! Let me help you down!" That's one kind of mother. Another mother controls herself and says, "Okay, jump."

At this age it is very important what kind of physical education a child gets; and the mother is the physical educator. The girls who are now in your college classes are the physical educators of tomorrow's preschool child. What does this jump mean to the child? Obviously, the only way it can express itself is by doing something within its ability. Modern psychology has taught us that very early in life we develop our feelings of self-worth, our feelings of acceptance or non-acceptance of self.

It is important to that child to jump, to feel it is somebody. Long before it can say, "I am somebody," it feels that way. If it is constantly told, "No, no, no, let me help you down; you can't do that; you will hurt yourself," what kind of a child are we raising? Here is the great remaining "gold mine" for physical education to exploit in its effort to influence the character, the personality, the traits or courage, or whatever you want to call them-of the adult to come. As the twig is bent, so grows the tree. It is also true that one who has never learned to accept himself, cannot accept others, because he will project on others the feelings he has about himself.

We must help to bring such experiences into the lives of more children long before they come to school. Watch kids in the first and second grade when their classmates urge them to attempt a daring feat. Some come running and then turn black; others go to it with abandon. They may trip but what's the difference, they go on. Similarly some adults are constantly holding back while others are trying. We must touch the lives of these young children, through our present high school and college girls, the mothers of tomorrow. This is physical education for the pre-school child.

Then there is the first time a child played in a game with official rules where one might have gotten away with something when the official wasn't looking or when the teacher was not very observant. That was a significant experience. Was there then a coach who said, "This does not go; you've got to play the right way or you don't play." Was there someone back there who gave that boy the first real feeling of respect for rules, perhaps connecting it with diencephalic pain connected through the prefrontal lobes to the ideas in the cortical part of the brain when he said, "This thing doesn't go! If you don't play right, you're out! You're a disgrace!" For this reason there is no such thing as "Just a kid's basketball game that doesn't count." The first game is perhaps the most important one.

These significant experiences in the lives of youngsters that may start them in one direction or another, are a challenge to us in physical education. They make it important that even in elementary school there be somebody in charge who knows the rules and sportsmanship, and who is both capable and alert to make sure that the right thing happens.

Moving up a bit, let us look in on a high school. Visualize a boy sitting in a literature class where Shakespeare must be read. What is he doing? His lips are moving a bit. Especially when the teacher is looking, he goes through motions of being interested; but somewhere in his subconscious he is thinking of something else. He has a bit of athlete's itch on one foot; so one foot is scratching the other. The bell rings and Henry-VIII goes out the mental window. This is no pretty picture of integrated activity. But watch this same boy in the closing minutes of a basketball game with the score tied and you will see the whole boy playing, completely integrated with but one purpose.

We've said a lot about the whole child going to school; but what do we do with the whole child? In the lower grades we can perhaps occupy him. Here they read a story and then act it out. But in that high school literature class, the boy's eyes and lips may be there, but the rest of him is most likely some other place. There is little that demands he give himself, totally. This leads me to say that an integrated activity is a significant experience.

Unfortunately, we have less and less of that as we go up the academic ladder in our schools. The only place where the average fellow still gets a totally integrating experience, one in which the whole individual acts, thinks, and feels together—eyes, ears, muscles, brain, glands—everything, is in the gymnasium or on the athletic field. Maybe this is why play is so important to people; this is why youngsters like it so much.

Too much of modern day life depends on the use of the eyes and ears only. But we know that ideas in our minds, concepts, if you wish to call them that, are composed of everything that comes into the cortex from the sense organs-from eyes and ears, yes, but these are not enough. What comes in from the muscles may often be just the feeling of sitting on one's seat. This does not ensure formation of a true-to-life concept because a related, true-to-reality proprioceptive component is lacking. The child that cannot distinguish between the moon, a cookie, and a ball that are held before it may grab for each but soon learns to distinguish between the moon, a cookie, and a ball that are held before it may grab for each but soon learns to distinguish between the moon on the one hand, and the cookie and the ball on the other when he can or cannot reach them or get his hands on or around them. Until he gets his hands around a ball he does not really know what a ball is and even though he can't get them around the moon, his appreciation of the roundness of the moon depends on the fact that he has had a ball in his hands. The third dimension experience, the depth dimension of our concepts comes to us from muscle and joint senses, i.e., the proprioceptive system. Too much of modern life is limited by two dimensions. Too much is just seeing picture and reading the printed page. It is short on muscle and joint experiences.

Elementary education is better in this important respect than is secondary and higher education except for laboratory work. Active out stories bring much more meaning to Macbeth or to Robin Hood than just reading the words. Could you imagine a nation going wild over a world's series game reported by radio if its people had never actually played some kind of ball game? Denied such experiences some people develop a deep-seated hunger for them, others have so often ignored the feeling that they have lost the craving.

Many people cannot express their feelings as did the artist. People find these concept-fulfilling experiences, not only in physical education activities, but also in gardening, in handicrafts, and in many other physical activities. This is terrifically important, lest we come to live in a completely unrealistic, flat world; and has far reaching significance.

Too often, instead of doing the thing with our hands, we just write a check and somebody else gets the real experience. Thus deprived of bodily experiences with reality our concept forming mind suffers a kind of malnutrition due to a deficiency in the proprioceptive component of the diet of sensory experiences—the muscle and joint component. The resulting sickly formed concepts may account for some cockeyed thinking and failure to cope decisively with problems even in high places. In times of national and international crisis, a farmer, a foot soldier, a miner, or even a paper hanger may rise to replace the talkers. Probably combinations such as rail splitter-lawyer or carpenter-teacher dedicated to high values would be even better. In a time when such experiences are disappearing from urbanized American life our concepts may well become correspondingly "anaemic" and unrealistic. But this is no propaganda for a "back-to-the farm movement." The farm is also becoming push-button. It does argue for supplementing the unbalanced sensory diet of civilized life with consciously selected dosages of muscular experience.

There are other ways in which modern life destroys integration. If you get mad at somebody, you don't dare show it, lest you get into trouble, especially if he's your boss. But let's go to the zoo and stand in front of the monkey cage. Do something to make the monkey mad. There'll be no question about it, he'll display his anger so everybody knows it. We call this honesty. Let us call it integrity or "oneness." When John was a youngster a Jewish friend told him, "There's something about him he like. He is what we call one." It took him years to grasp the real meaning of what he said. He meant that he said what he felt and felt what he said. In this sense the monkey is also one.

Obviously, this does not happen regularly in modern life. You have had people call you wonderful and yet you were afraid to leave the room for fear of what they would say when you were gone. It's good that people don't always tell him what they think about him. He couldn't take it. This kind of behaviour is found only on one tiny twig of the animal tree. It's the schizic branch where man sits at the top where behaviour is split—where we say one thing when we feel another. It is civilization. One can have only a few friends to whom one can talk as he feels. How awkward it would be otherwise.

A young woman who in the summer of 1937 sat in class at the University of California gave the instructor a good idea. It was in the days when some of us swore at modern dance and others swore by it. She was all for it. "Tell me," the instructor said, "why are you so crazy about this modern dance?" She gave this very significant answer. Well, since I'm a woman, I'm supposed to act like a lady; I must take short steps and I have to be dainty whether I want to or not. But in modern dance I feel big, I can make a big movement and if I want to stamp, I can stamp. It's okay." Dance gave her the opportunity to do and feel as one. Dance gave her the wonderful feel of integration. Could we say that modern dance brings to man the healing balm of monkey wholeness?

But you don't have to do modern dance to get the feel of such as experience. You can get it with a minimum of activity. Will all of you please say, "flat." Now say "point" and move your lips back. Say "flat" and point your lips. It's true also in other languages. Always if you speak simple words like "up," "down," "flat," and "point," the face moves with it. I've discovered another interesting and related fact. If you ask a person to repeat the word "spitz" for instance, and he imitates the sound without knowing what he is saying he will very likely do it poorly. But if you tell him "spitz means point" he'll do a much better job. This reminds me of what I've been taught by my modern dance friends. They say, "If you imitate, it isn't modern dance. But if you feel it first and then do it, it's modern dance." This is the way the instructor learned the meaning of modern dance and how to understand the ladies who do it so well.

We men may get the same feeling in other ways. Recalling one case in which some young boys were playing football in a snow storm, over forty years ago. As offensive tackle it was the individual's job to block the opposing line men. Hitting the line again and again with almost bone crushing force with body, mind, and emotion all together hellbent with others on going in one direction, provided such an experience that one never forgets.

Similarly when a piece of wood connects squarely with horse hide and the ball goes places, the whole individual operating with split second perfection gets this feeling of togetherness. All of us have such experiences once in a while. Many of us don't have them often enough. One explanation for satisfaction gained from swatting a ball involves imagining it's your mother-in-law to get all the aggressions out of you. To anyone that is an unnecessarily complicated explanation. One can get something very direct from hitting the ball just right without anthropomorphizing the little sphere. It may help some people but not him. Perhaps this is a tribute to one's mother-in-law.

We don't yet fully understand the implications to mental health of thus constantly splitting ourselves rather than acting as one. It has not been proven, but it is felt fear that such continual splitting must weaken the force of one's personality. Continuous ambivalence or something approaching that must put a strain on the structure of mind. Efforts have been put to coin a companion term of "monovalence" or "univalence" but the nearest one can get to it is "integration" or "wholeness" as the contrasting condition that builds inner strength. When we centre attention on feelings we sometimes speak of mixed feeling. That is the feeling one is supposed to has when his mother-in-law drives his brand new Cadillac over a cliff. If we insist on taking mother-in-law for a ride in our analogies, then think of mother-in-law driving him old, decrepit Chevrolet on which he has plenty of insurance over the cliff. That would be all feelings going in the same direction.

If a given object or experience makes us feel two ways, for example, if an individual has to feel nice toward somebody and at the same time he do feel another way, this disintegrating. The boy who wants to win so badly that he's willing to do anything to win, even though his own code of ethics says it's wrong is having a disintegrating experience. It's like a woman falling in love with a married man. That's an awfully disintegrating experience because the object, the man, calls out two feeling in her—one which says "go" and the other which says "no". This tears things apart. But this need not be in sports. In good sports, properly coached, we learn to play hard and fair, to win-but not at any cost; if winning has not been pitched too high.

Obviously it is most important that the right kind of leadership is given to the youngsters at the time when feelings are tied up with what is right and wrong in sports. Then all goes together in the right direction.

Why are boys so crazy about playing ball or playing on a team? It isn't because they like to run around. It isn't only because they enjoy the game. There is something else about it. It is this feeling of being needed, this feeling of being a part of something that is greater than One's self and feeling important to it. These are significant experiences. These are the experiences that often keep a boy in high school when he otherwise would drop out. No doubt there are comparable experiences in the lives of girls, experiences that provide a genuine feeling of worth not for personal aggrandisement with arrogance, but in service to a group or to the school. We can provide many opportunities for such significant experiences to our young people. We must learn to make each such experience provide 100% significance in the finest sense possible. This happens best when somebody in position of leadership understands what should happen and helps it to go that way.

Athletes as a whole do their best work at about age 25. That's roughly when most of the athletic records are made. Skilled labourers reach their peak at age 35. Brain workers at age 45. Inventions come most commonly between the ages of 31 and 35. Poets and dramatists ripen between 44 and 50. Of course there are always exceptions, but these are the averages. And after 50 there is nothing left for us but to become philosophers. That explains why you asked me to speak, which, by the way, has also shown me another time when one can have a significant experience. That is when some big idea takes hold of one.

The older we get the more pieces should come to fit together to ensure for us a satisfying philosophy for our profession, for our life. The philosophy is the picture, the facts are the parts. The mind sits in front of the pieces, unhappy, until they begin to fit together. The mind wants to see the picture, it is confused by the disjointed parts. The bringing together of more and more facts into an ever enlarging consistent and satisfying philosophy of our task, of our profession, of our place in the larger scheme of things, is the most difficult and never ending task for the human mind. Progress in its accomplishment brings feelings of satisfaction commensurate with the significance of the experience.

RESEARCH IMPLICATION—THEN AND NOW

A discussion of the topic, Research-then and now, should begin with a clarification of terms. For "Then," two periods, in which research had a definite characteristic, have been selected. It is logical on this the seventy-fifth anniversary of our national association to begin the first "Then" in 1885 and, as will be seen later, to mark its close in the first decade of the twentieth century. There followed a period of transition from the one type of research to another which began in the 20's and extended to the 40's. This again was followed by a period of readjustment in research and it is interesting to note that during both transitional stages this country was engaged in war. "Now" will be considered as beginning in the 50's.

Was there research in each of these three periods and if so, what was its chief characteristic? What were the influences which shaped the investigation? It has been said, "Science owes many of its spectacular advances to improvement in methodology and the introduction of new techniques." As each period is summarized, these two factors, methodology and techniques, will be seen as important in research our field.

It will be well, as the three areas are surveyed, have in mind the meaning and the nature of research. Briefly, research is a search for truth. Note that the word is a combination of search and the prefix re-Current truth is scrutinized and re-examined to determine whether it is still true or whether a new statement should replace or expand the old. Steinhaus, in describing research to physical educators, said, "The methods of research, though endlessly different in their specific application, are fundamentally simple. Essentially they comprise four steps: (1) observation; (2) recording and treating the observed data; (3) generalization to the formulation of a theory; (4) testing the new formulation with further observations."

Looking now at the first then, were physical educators searching for truth in the late 1800's? Certainly they were making observations, were recording these, and to some degree treating the data. No well-trained physical educator in that day would begin classes until students had been measured and tested. In many an institution physical education classes did not begin until two or three weeks after the opening of school. This did not mean that the physical educator was idle; on the contrary, she was perhaps the busiest person on campus. From the time of the opening bell until the dinner hour, she was measuring heights, weights, sitting heights, girth of forearm, upper arm, necks, thighs, calves, length of arms and legs, strength of backs, legs, chests, and volumes of lung capacity. And if there was a right and left, both measures were taken.

The interest of the profession in this type of measure is show in the appointment of committees on Statistics and Measurement, the first in 1885, the last in 1903. The final report of this committee was made at the national convention in 1905, thus providing a closing date for this Anthropocentric Age. These successive committees, during their quarter century of existence, suggested and approved items which were to be tested or measured; at one time the list included 50 items. Thus, making observations, the first step in research as listed by Steinhaus, was a large scale, almost universal, operation.

Did the physical educator carry out the second step, recording and treating the observed data? With the limited statistical techniques which were available, scores were recorded and treated. Based on hundreds and even thousands of measures, chart showing averages and percentile ranges were published for men by Hitchocock, Sargent and Seaver, and, for women, at wellesley, Oberlin and the University of Nebraska. Each student was given a chart of these group measures and on it were plotted his own scores, thus showing individual standing in comparison to his peers. Using these charts, the instructor planned a program of gymnastic exercises for each student. This profile of individual status and needs is today considered sound and desirable. Our profession can take pride in these pioneer procedures and would do well to continue them. The items measured will differ; the general procedures are sound.

Reports on gains made as a result of participation in physical education would be as commendable and as desirable in 1960 as it was in the beginning of the century. Each of us would like to present such figures, but we can be assured that whatever the gain, questions would be asked. Are the gains significant and can they be attributed to physical education classes? Did the Wisconsin student of 1912 gain in leg strength because she exercised in the gymnasium or because each day she climbed the hill on the Madison campus?

From the treatment of the data, it can be assumed

that the physical educator implied that gymnastic exercises increased strength and lung capacity. This was an accepted theory before the observations were made; the theory was not tested. Research of this first then was limited to the first two of the four steps in research.

In research, facilities are important. There must be personnel capable of conducting investigations; there must be time for observation, for organizing data, time for thinking and theorizing; there must be space and there must be equipment for making the desired observation. This list does not name funds specifically, but it is obvious that if time, space and equipment are not adequate, often these lacks can be attributed to insufficient funds. Even adequate personnel may depends on the budget.

Equipment was not costly. The most expensive were the dynamometers, but these were long-lived. Many purchased before 1900 are usable today. Neither space nor time were problems. The entire department staff and the entire department space were available for the measurement period. Perhaps some staff member sat up all night to calculate averages without the aid of a calculator; yet college enrolments were small, as were those in secondary school and wholesale measurements in elementary schools were not common.

The last report of a national committee on Anthropomorphic marks a significant date in the Measurement of Man. It was in 1905 that a French psychologist, Alfred Binet, published his first series of tests to measure human intelligence. Binet made provisions of his tests up to the time of his death in 1911. Educators in this country were interested in the new device and during the first World War, with the availability of the service men, the first large scale measurement of intelligence was conducted with the administration of the Army Alpha Test. Binet's tests were revised for use in American schools, courses in measurement were added to psychology and education departments, and became a necessary part of teacher training.

By the 20's some colleges and universities offered an undergraduate major in physical education leading to a Bachelor's degree. In 1925, a national committee recommended that all directors and supervisors of physical education should have a bachelor's degree, and that all college teachers, with the exception of specialists, such as coaches and teachers of dance and swimming, should have equal preparation. With professional training in the colleges and universities, the student in physical education came in contact with the rapidly developing tests for mental ability. One of the early statisticians, McCall of Teacher College, Columbia University, enthusiastically proclaimed that anything which exists can be measured. Physical educators are not likely to ignore a challenge. If mental capacity and ability could be measured, why not motor ability, native and acquired? And so began the Motor Measurement Millennium.

Physical educators following the pattern set by psychologists and educators undertook the task of devising tests to measure human ability. Preliminary observations had already been made. It was and is common knowledge that individuals have motor abilities and that the degree of ability differs. Even a child in choosing players for his team makes his selection on a judgment of skill.

However, such judgments are not scored numerically and experts may disagree on ratings. Investigators undertook to find test situations in which numerical scores could be obtained and in which differences of judgment would be minimized.

Their methods of procedures in devising tests followed a general pattern; analysis of the elements of the skill, selecting and devising situations in which performance could be objectively scored and then subjecting the scores to statistical analysis. Young and Moser's presentation of the process of obtaining a battery of tests to measure basketball ability illustrate these steps. The elements contributing to successful performance are according to their analysis, (1) ability to handle the ball, throwing and catching; (2) ability to handle the body in relation to the ball, to move quickly, to change direction, to jump; (3) ability to make baskets. As a result of the ingenuity of the investigators and search through basketball literature, 36 situations were listed as possible measurement devices. These were administered to classes and on the basis of subjective evaluation and statistical treatment, seventeen tests were studies more intensively. Finally, on the basis of statistical evidence of reliability and validity, five tests were recommended as a battery which would measure the ability to play basketball.

Investigators of motor ability have generalized from their observations and treatment of data, step three in methods of research. Many such batteries to measure ability in various sports were presented in this period, as were measures of more general abilities. The fourth step in research, testing the new formulation with further testing, was not common. Most of the batters were the outcomes of Master's these and Doctoral dissertations.

During the 20's and 30's, there had been a rapid increase in the number of colleges offering graduate majors in physical education. In the first decade of the century, three schools offered courses leading to an advanced degree-Columbia, Oberlin and Sringfield College. During the 20's, eleven more schools offered such courses and by 1942 the number had increased to fifty-six. Had it not been for the need of presenting a thesis for the these degrees, perhaps such batteries as Brace's Motor Ability Test, Humiston's and Scott's Tests of Motor Ability, Dyer's Test for Tennis, and the French and Cooper's Volleyball tests and many others would not have been developed. Once a battery had been proposed and the thesis completed, there was no demand for the fourth step of further testing and evaluation of the hypothesis.

Not only was there no demand for this step, there was often active opposition. Survivors of the Anthropometric Age were still members of the teaching staff; for many of them such terms as reliability and validity, standard deviation and correlation had little meaning. Development of test batteries took precious time from teaching. The measures of this period never were used as universally as were the anthropometric and strength measures. For the staff members reluctant to us the new devices, these years were anything but a millennium.

With disagreement within the profession, there was no longer time allotted to research projects. Time was available only for the graduate student because it was a part of the study load. There was little demand for special research equipment. The batteries were devised for use in classes, and equipment for testing was limited to that which was needed for the game itself.

Some insight into the facilities which would stimulate research was obtained in 1937 from a questionnaire which Dr. Frances Hellebrandt sent to all member institutions of the National Association of the Directors of Physical Education for College Women. Replies were received from 91 schools and of this number 10 indicated that faculty members had a definite time on their schedules for research. In two cases the amount was not defined; in one college, it ranged from 1 to 4 per cent; in seven colleges, from 10 to 30 per cent. Only two schools indicated that space was set aside for research; in 6, there was special research equipment; 7 had research funds in the budget-these were $10, $25, and $75; others were $300 and $650. Only two schools reported research assistants. There was one each on half-time in these schools and the salaries were $500 and $600 for 10 months.

The investigators who developed the test batteries were exploring a new field. They were usually experienced teachers, but not experienced in research. They learned techniques as they developed their problem. These advisors had little more experience than did the students; few had a doctoral degree. Perhaps the most valuable outcome of the period was not the research, but the training which it gave to students and faculty. These individuals were to become the investigators of the present period, the now of this discussion. They are among the chief influence which make now a period of promise.

The present is promising because research facilities are better than they have been at any time in our history. Facilities, as stated earlier, include personnel, time space, and equipment. This one situation will illustrate the status of departments offering advanced degree. Some will be better equipped than is the example, some not as well.

First, the personnel. In 1930, there were on the staff one doctor of medicine, four women with Master's degrees, and the remainder of the staff had bachelor's degrees. Today, there is one doctor of medicine, four staff members have Doctor of Philosophy degrees, and, in general, only those women who have Master's degrees are taken on as full-time staff members. The qualifications for scientific investigation of the staff are now vastly superior to those of the 1930's, not only because there have been longer periods of preparation, but because the training in research procedures through which the staff members achieved their degrees is superior to that which the 1930 staff had experienced.

Second, the time for research. In the 30's whatever research was done by staff members was done in addition to a full teaching load. Many a midnight hour and many Sunday was spent in the laboratory and office attempting to follow some line of investigation intriguing at the time. Today, the department is attempting to develop a schedule which will include time for research as a part of the teaching load. Each staff member of professorial rank, and there are ten of these—three full professors and three associate and four assistant—will have such time for a given period. If at the end of the period she has demonstrated no drive for investigation, research time will not be allowed.

Frequently, research grant makes possible additional time. At present, such arrangement has made a 40 per cent reduction in one staff member's teaching load.

Research assistants can also be considered as adding to the staff member's research time, for these assistants do the routine work and take over many details of projects, thus enabling the staff member to accomplish more in the investigations. In the 30's there was one half-time assistant in the department; today there are eight. Three of these are supported by university funds, not considered a part of the department's budget, and five are supported by grants from off-campus organizations. Thus, it might be said that the research time is equivalent to the total load of at least six people.

Third, the space. In 1930, there was no space which the investigator could consider his own. Today, there are two large laboratories assigned to research projects. In addition, when the study demands, the entire staff is cooperative in making available space which is ordinarily used for other purposes. In a recent study which involved volume measures of the human body, tank was set up in one of the gang showers because a ready supply of water and a drain to carry off the water was needed. Another study required the use of the gymnasium for a two day period. Not only did the instructors of classes give up the space allocated to them, but they acted as assistants in that two day project, as members of their classes were measured in the overarm and underarm throws and in the standing broad jump.

The projects of one of the staff is concerned with strength studies. The dynamometers purchased in the early part of the century are still available, but the investigator prefers the tensiometer. That was purchased some ten years ago, and for the past six years that investigator has moved the testing table and the tensiometer to a neighbouring elementary school where 8 muscle groups have been measured on the same group of children during that period. At other time the equipment is used for studies with college students.

There are also ergographs for measuring the among of work which can be accomplished if a muscle group is exercised until fatigued. The distance a load is lifted and the time for lifting are recorded on another piece of equipment. These provide means of studying and comparing methods of improving strength.

For measurement of energy expenditure in exercise, there are Douglas bags to collect expired air. There are recorders to measure the intake of oxygen. These have long been used by physiologists.

In one of the laboratories, a small space has been insulated to permit electromyographic studies. It has long been recognized that a logical analysis of muscle action is not a valid picture of functioning muscles. Except for studies of walking, there have been no sound reports of muscle action in the skills which comprise physical education curricula. A recent electromyo-graphical study reports an observation which is of interest to those attempting to develop motor skill. It was found that when the free foot was planter flexed, the initial activity appeared in the peroneus lounges if the performer thought of pushing the forefoot downward.

On the other hand, if the performer thought of bringing the heel upward, the resulting planter flexion was initiated by contraction of the soleus. This suggests that the idea which is in the mind of the performer may be important in bringing into action the desired muscles and could be important in bringing into action the desired muscles and could be important to all teachers of motor skill.

And last in this list is the photographic equipment. Picture of motion taken at high speeds are essential for the physical educator as is the microscope for the biologist. Most descriptions of sports skills and locomotor skills are based on what the eye can see or on what the performer thinks he does. Both have been shown to be erroneous. Our equipment includes a 16mm, camera, which can expose 4,000 frames per minute and which is equipped with a wide one inch lens and a three inch lens. For studying film, there is a time-motion study projector, by which one frame can be projected for unlimited time without danger of burning the film and which can be turned by hand.

It can also be run at various speeds, forward or backward. More satisfactory for tracing film is the Recorder. Six of these are in our laboratory, three of which expose three frames at a time; the others, one frame. The projection is at table height convenient for tracing, and the film can be turned forward or backward by a handle within easy reach.

The ball velocity was measured from the film also and was 98.5 feet per second. The slight difference of 3.5 feet per second could be due to error in measurement or to failure to include some contributing factor.

Analysis of the joint action in the standing broad jump has shown that the action cannot be understood if the explanation is vigorous extension of hip, knee and ankle. Film study shows that the knee extensors and gravitational force are the main contributors to projection of the body. Ankle and hip extension maintain the direction of projection. To see that the downward force of gravity can pull the foot upward is to gain in appreciation of the Wisdom of the Body in motor performance, as Cannon saw that wisdom in physiological functioning in the early part of this century.

Film study shows that the performer uses joint action of which he is not aware. If these actions are not voluntarily controlled, how is the movement brought about? A possible explanation is that the human nervous system is equipped with inherent motor patterns, that the voluntary part of the skill is only the decision to perform and that the details of the act are taken over by that part of the nervous system which is below the level of consciousness. Inherent patterns have been recently studies in forms of life other than Man. Lorenz has indicated that patterns are inherited as surely as are physical features and Sperry has suggested that an affinity between specific muscles and specific neurones determine possible coordinations. Broer has shown pictorially the similarity of pattern in underarm throw, the volleyball and the badminton serve; in the overarm throw, the badminton clear, and the tennis serve; in the sidearm throw, the tennis drive and batting. If such patterns are inherent in Man, how early do they appear?

In observation of boys of pre-school age, we have found in a three year old the sidearm, overarm, and the underarm pattern in well established coordination. Teaching may well begin with the basic pattern, rather than with a description of detail.

These many avenues of study make possible a pooling of the findings of each in an attempt to look at motor development and skill from many angles. It is attack on the Unknown from many aspects rather than effort along one line only as was characteristic of the Anthropometric Age and the Motor Measurement Millennium. For example, when our photographic studies indicated that the principle projecting force in the standing broad jump was that due to contraction of the knee extensors, the staff member who was studying strength in the same subject reported that the correlation between the distance of the jump and the strength of knee extensors was greater than it was with either ankle or hip muscles.

Each line of investigation now requires special apparatus, which in many cases is designed for the project. Each investigator will develop technical methods which will result from long experience. Those who study by means of photography will have skills and information which differ from those of the student of strength. The department which was used as an illustration is only one of many. In each, there will be other special lines of investigation. Each investigator, confident in his ability to conduct research, will follow the leads suggested by his findings. Results from all parts of the country will attack the Unknown from many more aspects than will any one department. Research in physical education has reached maturity and the years ahead are indeed a Period of Promise.